SUSSEX INDUSTRIAL ARCHAEOLOGY:
A FIELD GUIDE

Sussex Industrial Archaeology: A Field Guide

Edited by
BRIAN AUSTEN, DON COX and
JOHN UPTON
On behalf of the
Sussex Industrial Archaeology Society

Phillimore

1985

Published by
PHILLIMORE & CO. LTD.
Shopwyke Hall, Chichester, Sussex

ISBN 0 85033 556 6

Typeset in the United Kingdom by:
Fidelity Processes - Selsey - Sussex

Printed and bound in Great Britain by
REDWOOD BURN LTD.
Trowbridge, Wiltshire

CONTENTS

LIST OF PLATES

INTRODUCTION

In the sixteenth and seventeenth centuries the Sussex Weald and the adjoining areas of Kent and Surrey was a major iron-producing region. This industry was however in decline by the beginning of the eighteenth century and expired completely a century later. Thus was eliminated the only major challenge to agriculture in the economy of the County. Agriculture itself is however a generator of craft industry and many small enterprises flourished on the basis of serving the needs of farming communities and small market towns which characterised the County. The rise of the seaside spa from the mid-eighteenth century, and especially the rapid growth of Brighton, provided a new focus of economic activity, greatly stimulated once the main railway line from London was open throughout in 1841. In one respect the railway was a destroyer of craft industry, allowing cheaper machine-made and standardised products to be brought into the area to undercut locally-made manufactures. The craft industries that characterised Sussex were however, in many cases, those that were unsuited to early mechanisation and these continued well into the railway age. As they gradually faded in the late nineteenth and early in the present centuries new employment developed in transport and the service industries, while the advent of electric power and technically sophisticated products requiring small material but high labour content enabled industry to expand rapidly in south-east England near to markets in Europe and good port facilities. The dominance of this area in the field of air transportation and Britain's link with Europe through the E.E.C. has reinforced this trend to light industry and service trades. In these developments Sussex has fully shared.

The pages that follow list the most significant industrial monuments to be found in the counties of East and West Sussex. All the structures listed were standing at the time that the text was completed, but demolition of items of industrial archaeological interest can take place at very short notice. This emphasises the importance of a society like the Sussex Industrial Archaeology Society dedicated to the recording of industrial sites before the evidence is destroyed beyond recovery. A policy has been adopted of selecting for this book only those sites which are accessible to the public or can be viewed from a public road or right of way. The few sites that are exceptions have been indicated in the text. Often in the case of buildings only the exterior can be examined without the prior permission of the owner and visitors are asked to respect the rights of occupiers to privacy and freedom from trespass.

The book has been compiled from information supplied by members of the Sussex Industrial Archaeology Society, with a specialism in particular fields. The contributions of the following are gratefully acknowledged:

Alan Allnutt	Engineering structures, bridges, piers, canals
John Bagley	Airports
Molly Beswick	Brickworks
John Blackwell	Railways
Martin Brunnarius	Windmills
Keith Donaldson	Bus transport
John Farrant	Harbours and public utilities
D. F. Gibbs	Upper Ouse Navigation
Frank Gregory	Mills
John Haselfoot	Sites in the Hastings area
Edward Henbery	Ifield Mill
Peter Holtham	Breweries
Frederick Sowrey	Airports
H. J. F. Thompson	Sites in the Littlehampton area

Other information and topics were contributed by the editors. Photographs unless otherwise acknowledged were supplied by John Upton and Don Cox compiled the maps.

Further information regarding the activities of the Sussex Industrial Archaeology Society can be obtained from the Hon. Secretary, R. G. Martin, 42, Falmer Avenue, Saltdean, Brighton BN2 8FG.

1. PUBLIC UTILITIES

GAS AND ELECTRICITY

Brighton can claim to have the oldest continuous supply of electricity in the county. This was followed shortly after by undertakings at Hastings and Eastbourne. Little remains however except a few buildings such as those at Worthing (TQ 151030) and Brighton (see below).

1.01 Brighton Generating Station   TQ 310045
The SEEB depot between North Street and Bread Street includes some buildings of the original Brighton Corporation generating station built in 1891. This was superseded by Brighton 'A' power station built c. 1904 on the eastern arm of Shoreham Harbour opposite Southwick and demolished in the 1970s.

1.02 Heathfield Natural Gas Supply   TQ 581206
A standpipe is all that remains of this work, built in 1896 after natural gas was discovered whilst drilling for water for the London, Brighton & South Coast Railway. Heathfield station was lit by gas until the 1930s and for a short time commercial supply was also made to the town.

WATER SUPPLY

Rural communities in many cases were not supplied with piped mains water until the present century and surviving examples of wells and pumps designed to supply village communities are not uncommon. The most attractive are probably:

1.03 East Marden − thatched roofed well   SU 807146
On a triangle of grass in the road junction outside the church.

1.04 Ringmer Village Pump   TQ 449126
At a corner of the green near the edge of the A 265. The well was sunk and the pump erected in 1883.

1.05 Newick Village Pump   TQ 419213
On the village green beside the A 272. Erected in 1897 by the inhabitants to commemorate Queen Victoria's Jubilee.

1.06 Sedlescombe Pump and Wellhouse   TQ 782179
Of 1900 in the middle of the village green.

1.07 Northiam Village Pump   TQ 830245
On the Green beside the A 28 road. Erected in 1907.

Where wells had to be sunk at great depth through chalk, animal power was used to raise water. Examples of such animal gins are listed in section 3.

Some early examples of urban supply systems survive in the form of:

1.08 Winchelsea Town Well   TQ 906175
In Castle Street. The wellhouse is thought to have been constructed in 1831.

1.10 Coultershaw water pump. (M. Coviello).

1.09 Rye Water Cistern and Tower   TQ 922203

Located in the north-east corner of St Mary's churchyard. It was built in
1735 as part of a general scheme approved in 1730 for improving the
town's water supply. The cistern, which is below ground level, is oval in
shape, of brick and has a capacity of approximately 20,000 gallons. It is
surmounted by a brick tower with a truncated dome. A hand pump of
1826 is situated in front of the cistern.

1.10 Coultershaw Water Pump   SU 972194

Beside the A 283 1½ miles south of Petworth. It was installed in 1782 by
the 3rd Earl of Egremont to supply water from the River Rother for his
own private use. The water was pumped through pipes to two reservoirs at
Petworth. Townspeople might, on application, have been allowed to connect to this supply. The pump in its present form is powered by a later
breast shot water wheel. It has recently been restored to working order by
members of the Sussex Industrial Archaeology Society and is protected by
the erection of a nineteenth century barn building over it. The public may
view the pump on the first and third Sunday of each month during the
summer.

1.11 Arundel Water Pump   TQ 018077

Near Swanbourne Lake on the Arundel Estate. The turbine which powered
the pump is housed in a flint-faced brick, gothic revival building, now
roofless, which may be of the same date (1844) as the reservoir that it fed
on the hill above the town. Two triple throw pumps were used for this
supply.

Large urban centres by the nineteenth century required much more
sophisticated water supply arrangements. A good example of such an
urban supply is to be found in the **Goldstone Pumping Station** at Hove
which now houses the British Engineerium (see 8.09).

1.12 Brede Pumping Station   TQ 814178

Built in 1903 in connection with the water supply to Hastings. It originally
housed two 410 h.p. Tangye steam driven triple expansion engines supplied in 1904, of which one survives. Another building houses a 420 h.p.
Worthington Simpson triple expansion engine of 1941. A 457 mm (18 in.)
gauge railway originally carried the coal from Brede bridge, where it was
unloaded from barges, to the works. The line of the track can still be
traced.

SEWERAGE

1.13 Brighton Interceptor Sewer   TQ 314038

Built by Sir John Hawkshaw 1871–74. It comprises 13 miles of 2.2 m and
2.5 m diameter brick-built circular sewer, intercepting all the old sewers
which originally discharged directly on to the beach. The outfall, five
miles east of the town at TQ 393013, is taken well out to sea. It can handle
up to 15 million gallons per day. The brickwork is of a very high standard
and in excellent condition. Part of the system can be visited at low spring
tides on summer evenings and parties wishing to see it should apply to
the Southern Water Authority.

2. INDUSTRIES

BREWERIES

Beer is produced by adding hot water to ground malt in a 'mash-tun', boiling the resultant wort in a 'copper' with hops and often adding sugars, cooling, fermenting by the action of yeast for about five days and finally racking into casks or bottling. Once there were over 150 breweries in Sussex ranging from the small publican brewer producing for his own retail sale to large concerns which had evolved from takeovers and mergers. Many premises survive, their strong construction making them ideal for other uses. Most can be easily recognised by their chimney, louvred roof and 'tower' outline. Examples are:

2.01 Brighton, Black Lion Street   TQ 310040

Only a small portion of Chapman's Brewery survives having ceased brewing about 1902. The brewery was founded in 1545 by Deryk Carver who was burnt at the stake at Lewes in 1555 for his faith. It is reputed to be the oldest building in Brighton after the parish church and possibly the oldest brewery in the country. Fremlins of Maidstone used it for many years as a store until the site was bought by developers in 1968 and most of the buildings demolished.

2.02 Brighton, Dyke Road   TQ 307044

The brew-house of Henry Smithers' North Street Brewery survives. The date in the brickwork refers to the rebuilding in 1900. The premises extended westwards under the present Marks & Spencers stores and were closed in 1928.

2.03 Portslade Village, South Street   TQ 255063

Most of Dudnet & Son's tower brewery survives. The ownership and date of the building is recorded by the inscription 'D & S 1881' at the base of the chimney. The original premises are across the road to the west. The business was taken over in 1921 by Smithers of Brighton who brewed here until 1928. Later, the premises were used by a brewer of table beer until 1938. The present owner is Le Carbone (Great Britain) Ltd.

2.04 Worthing, Warwick Road   TQ 153026

A tower brewery with cold liquor tank at the top. Brewing by Harry Chapman ceased both here and at Burgess Hill when the company was sold to the Kemp Town Brewery of Brighton.

2.05 Lewes, Harvey's Brewery   TQ 420103

Situated by the River Ouse, and has been brewing for nearly 200 years. The brew-house was rebuilt in 1880 but the original Georgian fermenting room remains. A 28 h.p. side-valve steam engine installed for pumping a hundred years ago is kept in reserve should the modern electric pumps fail.

2.06 Lewes, Beard's Star Lane Brewery   TQ 414102

Situated in Fisher Street. Brewing ceased in 1959 and the company now supplies beer brewed by Harveys. Parts of the brewery are believed to date

2.05 Harvey's Brewery, Lewes

back to the reign of Charles II. Here is also a small steam engine built in Lewes over a hundred years ago.

2.07 Lewes, Southdown Brewery   TQ 421105
Brewing ceased in 1920 when the company was taken over by Tamplins of Brighton who used it as a store. Most of the buildings, including the nineteenth century classical style counting house, remain in Thomas Street, Cliffe.

2.08 Horsham, King & Barnes Brewery   TQ 168308
Following the merger of the two companies in 1906 brewing was continued at the former's brewery in the Bishopric. James King had started as a maltster here in 1860. G. H. Barnes took over the East Street Brewery in 1878. These premises have since been demolished.

2.09 Hailsham, Battle Road   TQ 589101
Brewing by Herbert Lynn ceased before the last war. The date 1887 in the brickwork refers to the rebuilding. Some of the original premises dating back to 1808 survive nearby.

2.10 Newick, High Street   TQ 418214
Brewing ceased in the First World War. The initials and date 'J. H. 1882' refer to the rebuilding under Joseph Hammond. The brewery owned no public houses and only one off-licence but did a good trade during the construction of the Bluebell Railway. The premises are now owned by Stonegate Farmers, having previously been a jam factory, an ice cream works and a piano store.

2.11 Lindfield, High Street   TQ 346254
The Durrant family owned the *Stand Up Inn* (now *The Linden Tree*) and the brewery situated behind. Brewing is thought to have ceased in the 1920s. The octagonal slate roofed gin house, brick chimney and sheds survive.

2.12 Hurstpierpoint, Cuckfield Road   TQ 280167
J. E. Couchman brewed here until 1915 when the company was taken over by Smithers of Brighton. The premises are now used by the Maxim Lamp Works.

2.13 Frant, Ware's Brewery   TQ 605360
Brewing by George Ware ceased soon after being taken over by Flowers of Stratford-upon-Avon in 1954. The premises survive being used by Wards Invalid Carriages Ltd.

2.14 Uckfield, London Road   TQ 474216
J. Knight ceased brewing here before the First World War. The premises survive to the north of a terrace of old cottages behind an oak tree. A plaque on the wall inscribed 'Rebuilt June 1887 S & Co' refers to an earlier owner Silvester & Co.

MALTHOUSES

Malt, an essential ingredient in the production of beer, is produced by the maltster first steeping barley in a cistern of water for 48 hours. After the water is drawn off the barley is spread on the floor and allowed to germinate for between 7 and 14 days. Before the malt tax was repealed in 1880 the barley was required to be held in an area called the 'couch' so that the Excise could measure the volume prior to flooring. The malt is finally dried in the kiln at various temperatures depending on the kind of beer to be produced. Although no malting is carried out in Sussex today, many malthouses survive, easily recognisable by their rows of small windows on one or more low floors, and the drying kiln with its steep roof topped by a cowl. Examples are:

2.15 Brighton, South Road, Preston   TQ 302064
A single floor building 8.1 m long with a square kiln, built to provide malt for the adjoining Preston Brewery which was in use until the 1880's.

2.16 Brighton, Southover Street   TQ 316050
Built by Tamplins to supply malt to their nearby Phoenix Brewery, which has recently been demolished, the site being now used as a depot.

2.17 Brighton, Cheltenham Place   TQ 313046
A two floor building now used as a warehouse with an office in the kiln. Formerly used to provide malt for Smithers' North Street Brewery.

2.18 Brighton, London Road   TQ 312055
Now the Duke of York cinema. Most easily recognised from the south, viewed from the fire station that was built on the site of Henry Long-hurst's Amber Brewery which was demolished in 1901 for road widening. The business had been taken over by the Kemp Town Brewery, Brighton.

2.19 Lewes, Southover High Street   TQ 411096
A small malthouse, situated opposite Anne of Cleves House, built to supply Verrall's Southover Brewery, some remains of which can be traced farther west opposite the *Swan* public house.

2.20 Lewes, The Maltings   TQ 414102
Situated to the north of the castle and built by J. Langford to supply his Castle Brewery. The premises were later sold to E. Beard & Son to supply the nearby Star Lane Brewery. The Maltings now belong to the East Sussex County Council.

2.21 Arundel, Queen Street   TQ 021068
Now Hares Garage. A rectangular kiln exists together with an oast kiln. It is thought to have been built by George Puttock in the eighteenth century.

2.22 East Grinstead, Station Road   TQ 390385
Built to supply John Dashwood's Hope Brewery that until 1918 brewed in London Road on a site opposite the malting and now occupied by the fire station. The malthouse has now been converted and is used by the British Legion.

BRICK, TILE AND POTTERY MANUFACTURE

Of the 180 brickyards and brickfields marked on the 1898 O.S. 6 in. maps of the county little evidence remains, most of the sites being either levelled and returned to agricultural use, or more often developed as housing estates.

2.23 Berwick Brickworks   TQ 527075
The derelict remains of this hand-made brickworks may be seen from the B2108 road opposite the car park to Arlington Reservoir. Three up draught kilns 8.5 m by 3.7 m and 3.3 m high with 10 firing openings each

2.4.1. Water dawn Oat Laichmunche. Bricks during prior to firing.

side, a raised pug mill containing an electrically-driven Berry's patent brick machine approached by a ramp, tunnel driers, workshops and sheds still remain standing.

2.24 Ashburnham Brickworks   TQ 684161
A double Scotch kiln fired from beneath, a tile drying shed and brick-built workshop still remain. The sand and loam was dug from an adjacent field where the stepped soil layers are still visible. This estate brickworks closed down in 1968, being the last wood-fired brick kiln in the country to operate.

2.25 Keymer Brick & Tile Works, Burgess Hill   TQ 323193
The extensive site contains several ranges of kilns, including beehive down-draught ones, and is a reminder of the clay-working industries which resulted in the growth of the town. The early nineteenth century workers' cottages in nearby Nye Road were possibly associated with the works.

2.26 Warnham Brickworks   TQ 171344
An old-established brickworks, originally the Sussex Brick Co., later the Sussex & Dorking Brick Co. and now part of Redland Bricks Ltd. It lies to the east of the railway just north of Warnham station. A terrace of brick cottages with tile-hung upper storeys beside Warnham station were possibly workers' cottages built by the Company.

2.27 Southwater Brickworks   TQ 158260
All that is left of this once extensive works of the Sussex & Dorking Brick Co. is an old clay pit, now filled with water, just north of the disused railway.

2.28 Hastings Brickworks, Guestling   TQ 841158
High quality Fairlight clay is dug on the site and contains virtually no stones so that only simple crushing and consolidation to remove air is required before passing to the brickmaker. The hand-made bricks are dried in oil-heated chambers and finally passed to one of two similar oil-fired beehive (downdraught) kilns. Each kiln holds 30,000 bricks, the firing cycle taking about ten days.

2.29 Pitsham Brickworks, Midhurst   SU 878198
One of the few remaining sites where hand-made bricks are produced. Two separate installations with different firing methods are in use — an open clamp containing 100,000 bricks which is fired in the summer, and a downdraught barrel kiln which can be used all the year round, having a capacity of 23,500 bricks. Firing takes between 54 and 72 hours and consumes eight tonnes of coal.

2.30 Estate Brick and Tile Works, Brightling   TQ 687223
A brick-built shed and Scotch updraught kiln still survive on the site but are heavily overgrown. The site can be seen from the track leading off the lane from Oxleys Green.

2.31 Freshfield Lane Brickworks, Danehill   TQ 385262
Established as an estate brickworks in 1899. Bricks were still being made by hand until the introduction of machinery in 1928. At present bricks are produced by machine from clay dug on the site and clamp fired under cover, each clamp containing one million bricks.

2.32 Ebernoe Common Brickworks, Kirdford   SU 979274
The remains are especially important as they include a complete late

3.99 Pitsham brickworks, Midhurst

2.31 Freshfield Lane brickworks, Danehill

Mixing machinery, Eastfield Lane brickworks, Deepcliff

2.32 Remains of kiln, Ebernoe Common brickworks, Kirdford

2.39 Kiln stokeholes, Ebernoe Common brickworks, Kirdford

2.33 Piddinghoe pottery kiln before rebuilding

2.33 Piddinghoe pottery kiln after restoration

eighteenth century updraught kiln with twin stoke holes. The site has been scheduled as an industrial monument and is currently being restored and undergrowth cleared. The kiln is situated a few metres to the west of the footpath leading from the church.

3.33 Pottery Kiln, Piddinghoe   TQ 433032
An early nineteenth century updraught cupola type of pottery kiln. The kiln tapers toward the top and has a central opening flue intact. There are two firing tunnels under. This is the only recorded survival of this type of kiln in Sussex. The cone was rebuilt by the Sussex Industrial Archaeology Society in association with the Lewes Archaeological Group in 1981. It is easily seen in the garden of Kiln Cottage on the east side of the A275 just north of Piddinghoe village.

CHALK QUARRIES AND LIME KILNS

2.34 Offham   TQ 400116
A large chalk pit in which are the substantial remains of four lime kilns, three round and one square. A tramway can be traced descending a steep scarp through two well preserved brick lined tunnels passing under the A275 adjacent to the *Chalk Pit Inn* to the site of a wharf on a feeder to the River Ouse. This was first used in 1809 and is the oldest railway in Sussex. It was disused by 1890.

2.35 Glynde   TQ 458086
At the right of the entrance to the quarry can be seen an old tunnel kiln, a square stone structure, adjacent to the tramway cutting which passes under the road and emerges by the station platform. The partly demolished remains of a large double tunnel kiln exist in the quarry. The site was first used in 1834 and lime burning ceased c. 1970.

2.36 Steam engine from Glynde   TQ 516124
A steam engine of c. 1880 which drove the crushing mill has been restored and may be seen with other interesting machinery at Milwards Farm, Laughton, a private museum, if prior permission to view has been obtained.

2.37 Chalk Pits Museum (Southern Industrial History Centre),
          Amberley   TQ 028118
At one time one of the largest lime-burning complexes in the county. Two series of continuous burning bottle kilns exist, one series being converted from an 18 chamber De Witt downdraught type. Lime burning is recorded at this site in the first half of the nineteenth century. It was closed in 1960 and is now leased to the Southern Industrial History Centre as an open-air educational centre (see 8.01 in the Museums section).

2.38 Duncton lime kilns   SU 961163
Three mid-nineteenth century brick and flint kilns side by side set into the steep chalk hillside. The kilns have double brick arches with grates set well back, the central one being larger than the others. They may be seen from the public bridle path 275 m from the A285 at the foot of Duncton Hill.

2.34 Offham, interior of lime kiln

2.36. Steam engine from Glynde lime quarry. Now at Milwards Farm,
Laughton in a restored condition

2.37 Lime kilns, Amberley, now part of the Chalk Pits Museum

2.39 Washington lime kilns   TQ 120123

Three kilns covered with undergrowth, two in fair condition and one, smaller than the others, in poor condition. They date from the nineteenth century and are faced with brick and chalk blocks. To reach the site take the old road south from the village and after about a quarter of a mile turn east along a cart track that runs uphill.

GRANARIES AND WAREHOUSES

2.40 Lewes Granaries   TQ 419101
South of Cliffe High Street on the west bank of the River Ouse are two granaries. These were substantially rebuilt after a fire in 1912, at which date barges still worked up to Lewes. Stricklands is slate hung with a lucarne on the landward side and Stevenson's is of red brick, rather altered in recent years.

2.41 Warehouses, Rye Strand   TQ 918202
Situated on the town quay. They are timber boarded on brick bases and have recently been renovated. The oldest, thought to date from 1736, was built from stone brought over as ballast from France. It is known as the 'Grist Mill' and is being preserved.

2.42 Corn Stores, Rye   TQ 918204
A large three storey nineteenth century building beside the level crossing on Ferry Road (B 2080) marked 'Foreman's Corn, Hop and Seed Stores'. Now used as a pottery.

2.43. Granary, Chichester   SU 863046
An imposing range of brick-built granaries dating from c. 1870 stand on the east side of Baffins Lane. Part has been converted to offices.

2.44 Granaries and Warehouse, Arundel   TQ 019070
Until well into the nineteenth century the bulk of the shipping entering the River Arun berthed at Arundel rather than Littlehampton and the warehouses and granaries on the west bank of the river, south of the bridge, are a testimony to the importance of the port. A particularly fine example, in flint and yellow brick with a slate roof, stands at the bottom of Arun Street and a double brick and timber one, now an antique market, stands in River Road.

GUNPOWDER MILLS

2.45 Battle
Gunpowder was made in Battle for nearly two hundred years, the water-powered mills being sited on the banks of the River Asten (now named Powdermill Stream). Five mills were built, Farthing (TQ 737147), House (TQ 742146), Peppering-Eye (TQ 743139), Lower Peppering-Eye (TQ 745136) and Crowhurst (TQ 758118). Peppering-Eye dating from 1676 is the oldest and here can be seen the site of the pond with bay still extant, the brick-lined leat and a later brick building used for corning (granulating) the gunpowder. The foundations of the magazine can still be traced in a nearby shaw at TQ 746138. At the House mills the proprietor's house stands together with the watch houses. Incorporating

2.41 Warehouses, The Strand, Rye

2.15 Watch house, gunpowder mills, Battle

stones and sulphur crushing stones can be seen built into the walls of a garage and outbuildings. The pond is still in water as is that of Farthing slightly higher upstream. Part of the building still remains at the Crowhurst site.

2.46 **Sedlescombe Mills**   TQ 781176

Gunpowder was also made at Sedlescombe, a branch of the Battle works. Incorporating stones, lying in the garden, may be seen from the footbridge over the stream.

2.47 **Brede Mills**   TQ 801192

The only remains of this once flourishing works is an incorporating stone placed at the end of the bay of Powdermill Reservoir.

2.48 **Maresfield Mills**   TQ 462231

This gunpowder manufactory was established in 1849 and worked until *c*. 1859. Apart from the large pond, originally a hammer pond, the only trace of this large works is an incorporating stone lying flat on the ground near the footpath.

MINES

2.49 **Gypsum Mines and Works, Mountfield**   TQ 720195

Apart from the gypsum mine there is an associated processing plant which manufactures plaster and plasterboard. Mining operations commenced *c*. 1870. With the opening of a new mine at Brightling, an aerial ropeway extending some 3½ miles was erected to carry the gypsum to the Mount-field works. The works is visible from several places along the lanes as is the ropeway where it crosses either over or under the road.

2.50 **Sand-mine, Pulborough**   TQ 063193

This mine, deserted for many years and much overgrown, consists of a series of galleries sloping gently some 25 m into the hillside, from which sand was extracted using the pillar and stall method.

THE WEALDEN IRON INDUSTRY

The major physical remains of this industry, which reached its height in the late sixteenth and seventeenth centuries, are a considerable number of hammer ponds with their associated bays. A very good series survive in St Leonard's Forest and include Hawkins Pond (TQ 217292), Hammer Pond (TQ 219289) and Slaugham Pond (TQ 248281). In each case a minor road runs across the bay and the drop necessary to provide adequate power and the quantity of water stored to ensure continuous production can be noted. The last blast furnace to operate was that at Ashburnham (TQ 685170) which closed in 1813 though its associated forge continued to work metal until *c*. 1820. At Ashburnham the masonry wheelpit and bay of seventeenth or eighteenth century date can be noted. Pieces of slag can be easily located in the lane leading to the site. Many of the products of the industry including cast iron firebacks can be seen in Anne of Cleves House, Lewes and Hastings Museum (see section 8), and cast iron grave memorials can be found in a number of Sussex churches and churchyards. Wadhurst (TQ 641318) has some thirty alone dating from 1617 to 1799, mostly let into the church floor.

Mansfield

2.51 Wealden iron industry — excavating Maynards Green blast furnace

3. MILLS AND GINS

WINDMILLS

Of the 88 extant windmill structures and remains in Sussex today, only 24 can be classed as accessible and of interest from an industrial archaeological point of view. Those omitted will be found listed in the book by Martin Brunnarius, *The Windmills of Sussex* (Chichester 1979).

Explanatory notes:

A *postmill* has a timber body containing all the machinery and is supported on a *post* and *trestle*. The whole mill revolves to face the wind.

A *smock mill* has a stationary timber tower containing the stones; the cap alone rotates and carries the sweeps.

A *tower mill* has a stone or brick tower.

Sweep is a Sussex name for a driving sail.

3.01 Battle (Calbec Hill Mill)   TQ 748166
A converted white smock mill with metalled tower and fantail. Erected in 1805 and worked until the First World War. In 1894 the smock was covered with zinc sheet which has preserved it remarkably well. The machinery was removed in 1920. The present owner has had dummy sweeps and a fantail fitted. West of the B 2092 on the approach to Battle from the north. Stands on private ground next to a public footpath.

3.02 Chailey (Heritage Mill)   TQ 386214
Externally renovated white smock mill with fantail. Built in 1830 at Highbrook 5½ miles north of here, moved to Newhaven 19 miles south in 1844, then to present site in 1864 by Samuel Medhurst of Lewes. Mounted on a single storey brick base. The mill worked until just before the First World War. Now part of the Heritage and maintained by them. Just north of the A 272 road on private ground near a public footpath.

3.03 Cross-in-Hand (New Mill)   TQ 558218
Fatigued white post mill with Sussex tailpole fan-tackle. Originally erected at Framfield, brought to Cross-in-Hand and rebuilt in 1855 on a site ¼ mile south-west of here. Moved to present site in 1868 by Samuel Medhurst of Lewes. Worked until 1969 and was the last windmill to grind commercially in Sussex. Restoration work is being undertaken by Mr. C. J. Newnham and Sons and it is hoped to have the mill open and in working order. Off the A 265 road in Cross-in-Hand village on private ground.

3.04 Icklesham (Hog Hill)   TQ 888160
Renovated black post mill with top fan and trolley steps. Erected in Pett in 1781 and moved here in 1790 where the mill worked until the late 1920s. Very picturesque privately owned mill and curved mill house may be seen from the lane between Icklesham and Winchelsea. Stands on private land off the road.

3.05 Mayfield (Argos Hill)   TQ 571283
Preserved white post mill with Sussex tailpole fan-tackle. Built in 1835 and

3.05 Mayfield — Argos Hill Windmill

worked until 1927. Although the mill cannot work nowadays all the machinery remains within. A fine milling museum is set out in the roundhouse. Well maintained in a restored condition by the Wealden District Council, Crowborough. May be viewed by appointment. West of the A267 road.

3.06 Nutley TQ 451291

Restored black open trestle post mill with tailpole and talthur. Erected here *c.* 1820 but contains timbers and machinery from a considerably older mill and might well be ranked as the oldest in Sussex on this basis. Last worked in 1908. Unique in its simplicity and the fact that this is the only open trestle post mill left in the county. All machinery is present and capable of 'controlled' grinding. This mill has been well restored and gained an Architectural Heritage Year Award in 1975. North of the Nutley to Duddleswell road. Park car on Ashdown Forest and walk the short distance back.

Open: Last Sunday in month, Easter till end of September, also Bank Holiday Sundays and Mondays.

3.07 Patcham (Waterhall Mill) TQ 292086

Cement faced brick tower mill with fantail. Built in 1885 by J. W. Holloway of Shoreham and worked until 1924. Subsequently converted into living accommodation but with the machinery drive and stones still *in situ* between the floors. This was the last windmill to be built in Sussex. Stands east of Dyke Road Crossroads, behind Brighton, on the way down Waterhall Hill in a private garden.

3.08 Polegate (Ovenden's Mill) TQ 582041

Restored red brick tower mill with white cap and fantail. Built in 1817 for Joseph Seymour. Worked by wind until the Second World War after which an electric motor was used. Finished working in 1965 when Albert Ovenden, the last owner, generously made the mill and ground over to the Eastbourne and District Trust for £1,000. The Trust have been able to bring the mill to a running condition with all tackle present. There is a fine museum in the malthouse and granary adjacent. Immediately west of A22 road along a short lane and surrounded by housing.

Open: Sundays from Easter till the end of October, Bank Holidays and also Wednesdays in August.

3.09 Punnett's Town (Blackdown Mill) TQ 627209

Rebuilt white smock mill with fantail. Brought here in 1857 from Biddenden in Kent after the post mill here was burnt. The mill was re-erected on a two storey base of sandstone hewn locally. Worked until the late 1920s, partially dismantled in 1935 and painstakingly rebuilt by the present owner Archie Dallaway to its present remarkable trim. A striking and attractive landmark north of the B2096 road. Stands on private land adjacent to a lane.

3.10 Rottingdean (Beacon Mill) TQ 366025

Externally renovated black smock mill. Erected in 1802 for Mr. T. Beard, and worked until the early 1880s. Originally owned by the Abergavenny Estates, now owned by Brighton Corporation and cared for by the village. A coastal landmark standing next to a public footpath on Rottingdean golf course.

3.08 Polegate Windmill

3.11 Stonecross   TQ 620043

White cement-faced brick tower mill with fantail reflecting some Kentish practice. Built in 1876 by Stephen Neve of Warbleton and worked until 1937. The mill now has only two sweeps and due to a broken cap cannot be winded. Maintained by the owner but not open to the public. Stands on private ground just south of the A27 road in Stonecross village.

3.12 West Blatchington   TQ 279068

Preserved black smock mill forming part of a complex of farm buildings. Erected on a square flint and brick base raised through existing farm buildings c. 1820. Ceased working in 1897. Painted by Constable in 1825. Modified and updated during its life. Many of the impressive frame and hursting members are thought to be old ship timbers and must pre-date the mill. Was owned by the Abergavenny Estates but now is in the care of Hove Borough Corporation and the Friends of West Blatchington Mill. Within the abutting barns a very tastefully laid out exhibition of milling bygones and related artefacts is to be found. Very easy to spot when approaching from Dyke Road Crossroads in a westerly direction. Standing on a green island, now surrounded by housing.

Open: Sundays, May till end of September.

3.13 Barnham   SU 968039

Sweepless remains of a black tower mill with white cap and fantail. Built c. 1828 of cement and brick rubble. Extensively re-worked in 1890 by J. W. Holloway of Shoreham. The mill finished working by wind in the early 1920s when a gas engine took over entirely. Standing in private grounds adjacent to the A2024 road through Barnham village.

Clayton Mills (Jack and Jill)

A well-known and unique pair of windmills on the South Downs.

3.14 Jack   TQ 304134

Partially restored large black cement faced tower mill with white cap and fantail. Built in 1866 by William Cooper of Henfield to replace Duncton post mill whose round house adjoins the mill tower. Worked until 1907. The machinery was completely removed in 1912 leaving only the wind shaft and part of the upright shaft. Stands on private ground and can be viewed only by special arrangement with Jill Windmill Preservation Society.

3.15 Jill   TQ 303134

Large white post mill with Sussex tailpole fantackle. Originally erected in Brighton 1821 and brought up to Clayton and rebuilt by Samuel Medhurst of Lewes c. 1852. Worked until 1907. Standing just to the west of 'Jack', Jill is very well situated for wind. Two storey round house. This mill is the subject of an extensive restoration programme to bring her to full working order by the Jill Windmill Preservation Society. Owned by the Mid-Sussex District Council. At present only open on fine Sundays during the summer and special open days. East of the A273 up a short lane at the top of Clayton Hill.

3.16 Earnley (Somerley Mill)   SZ 817893

Partially restored small smock mill with black Manhood peninsular top. Erected c. 1800, raised on to a single storey brick base and reworked in 1827. Last ground by wind in 1942. Most machinery still present. Was

3.12 West Blatchington Windmill

painted black or white by turns. A very interesting mill full of tackle and evidence of a long and useful life. Owned by the Stevens family for almost 100 years, now being restored by the present owners C. N. & P. Darby assisted by A. Pollard. Stands in a private garden close to the B 2198 Bracklesham road.

3.17. **Halnaker 'A'**   SU 920097

Externally renovated tile hung brick tower mill. One of the oldest remaining mills in Sussex, erected *c.* 1750 for the Goodwood Estates. Last worked in 1905. Restored in 1934 to appear as painted by Turner at the beginning of the nineteenth century with a hand winder only.

3.18 High Salvington (Durrington)   TQ 123067

Black post mill with tailpole *c.* 1745. High Salvington is perhaps the oldest mill now standing in Sussex but paradoxically nearly all the main timbers have been renewed in recent times which rather belies this. Worked until 1897, was a local attraction from 1910 or so and came into the hands of the Worthing Borough Council in 1959. At present the mill is undergoing extensive restoration. The Friends of Salvington Mill hope to re-open it in the not too distant future. Take the Bost Hill Lane west of the A 24 out of Worthing.

3.19 **Keymer** (Oldland)   TQ 321163

White post mill with tailpole and talphur built between 1755 and 1824. An attractive, well built mill re-worked by Boaz Medhurst of Lewes in 1873 to enable steam working in still weather. Owned by the Turner family for the greater part of its working life which ended *c.* 1914. Made over to the Sussex Archaeological Trust in 1927. Original octagonal brick round house, unique in Sussex. A restoration programme is being worked out by the Hassocks Amenity Association and some work has started. On greensand ridge between Keymer and Ditchling in a private garden beside a green lane, not accessible to cars.

3.20 **Lowfield Heath**   TQ 270398

Renovated white post mill with tailpole and talphur. This mill was in Surrey until boundary changes in 1974. Dates from *c.* 1762 and worked until 1880. Renovated in 1939. Revived once more in 1968 at the expense of the Surrey County Council and the S.P.A.B. West of the A 23.

3.21 **Selsey** (Medmerry Mill)   SZ 844934

Converted red brick tower mill with fantail. Built *c.* 1805. Worked until 1890 then fell into disrepair. Completely rebuilt by J. W. Holloway of Shoreham in 1907–8 then worked until the early 1920s by Faine & Co. Empty today, the base is used as a gift shop. Very prominent, to the west of Selsey village, on West Sands holiday complex.

3.22 **Shipley** (Vincent's Mill)   TQ 143218

White smock mill with fantail, maintained in working condition. Built by Grist & Steele of Horsham for Friend Martin in 1879. Came into the hands of Hilaire Belloc in 1906 and continued working until 1926. Very large mill (7.3 m across inside corners at base of smock) raised on a two storey brick base and is equipped with auxiliary drive for engine power. All the original tackle is in place and in working order. Vincent's Mill is open regularly and grinds when wind and miller permit. It is somewhat sheltered today and stands in a beautiful setting in the village of Shipley, south of the A 272.

Open 1st Saturday and Sunday of each month May till October.

3.23 Singleton Open Air Museum   SU 874128

Reconstruction of a nineteenth century hollow post pumping mill. This mill in its original form stood at Westham in East Sussex and was rebuilt here in 1975. Drive by bevel gears and upright shaft to two eccentric cams for lift pumps. Originally used to drain brick clay workings. Now pumps water from the mill back to the pond, wind permitting.

3.24 West Chiltington (Meeten Mill)   TQ 085181

Erected *c*. 1838 and refitted by W. Cooper of Henfield in 1865. Worked until 1922 when the machinery was removed and it was converted into living accommodation. Raised on a two storey brick base. The mill was originally hand winded, a pretty white fantail was employed latterly. Now privately owned. The mill may be approached by walking up the sunken lane.

WATERMILLS

Unlike windmills that are generally situated on exposed positions watermills tend to be sited in well hidden wooded valleys that are also private land. However we are fortunate in Sussex in having a number of mills that are available for all to see.

3.25 Batemans, Burwash (Park Mill)   TQ 671236

Eighteenth century brick and timber framed building with 3 m diameter overshot waterwheel and three pairs of stones. Owned by the National Trust and now in working order following restoration largely by members of the Sussex Industrial Archaeology Society. Usually grinding most Saturday afternoons during the summer months. Adjoining the mill is a Gilkes water turbine installed by Rudyard Kipling in 1902 to drive a dynamo to provide electric light for the house. This too is in working order.

Open every day except Friday, March to October.

3.26 Burton Mill   SU 979180

Large stone building built in 1781. Formerly had two waterwheels. These are now replaced by turbines which originally drove saw benches. Now a pair of millstones have been installed and the mill is grinding wholemeal flour which is sold on open days. Restored mainly by Sussex Industrial History Society members. Situated along a side road about one mile east of the A 285.

Open Saturdays and Sundays.

3.27 Ifield Mill   TQ 245364

On the site of a sixteenth century iron forge a cornmill was raised in 1683. Milling ceased in the late 1920s and the near derelict building together with the waterwheel have been restored by a volunteer group. It is hoped to restore the interior in the future. Crawley Museum Society lease the site and exhibitions of a local nature are planned. Can be seen from lane and footpath close by. Open by arrangement.

3.25 Mr. Sydney Ashdown dressing the runner stone, Batemans.

3.28 Lurgarshall Mill (Singleton Open Air Museum)   SU 874128
Small stone watermill with overshot iron wheel. Rescued and rebuilt at
the Museum where it can be seen at work. Mainly wooden machinery with
two pairs of stones. (See also 8.12).

3.29 Michelham Priory Mill   TQ 556093
Old timber framed building on brick base. The machinery was removed in
the 1920s and a turbine installed to generate electricity but this does not
survive. A waterwheel and machinery have recently been installed with one
pair of stones usually grinding wholemeal flour on Wednesday afternoons
during the season. Owned by the Sussex Archaeological Society.
    Open April to October.

3.30 Woods Mill, Small Dole, Henfield   TQ 218137
An eighteenth century building with an overshot wheel (penstock by Neale
& Cooper of Henfield dated 1854). Original hursting and stones no longer
survive but a small hurst with one pair of stones have been reconstructed
and are in working order. The owners, The Sussex Trust for Nature Con-
servation, use the remainder of the building for natural history displays.
    Open to the public from Easter to September (not Monday or Friday).

    The following interesting mills can be seen from adjacent public roads
or footpaths but are on private land and are normally not open to the
public.

3.31 Birdham Tidemill   SU 827013
Building now gutted and used as a store. Part of Chichester Marina.
Formerly had two waterwheels.

3.32 Bishopstone Tidemill   TQ 459002
Remains of the mill and cottages. Had three waterwheels that drove 15
pairs of millstones. Now only footings and wheel culverts remain. The
main reservoir lay to the east. Another was added to the west but has been
filled in by the owners, British Rail.

3.33 Bodiam Mill   TQ 826183
Only the waterwheel, in rather poor condition, remains at this mill site.
On west side of Bodiam to Staplecross road.

3.34 Brewhurst Mill, Loxwood   TQ 046311
Large nineteenth century mill containing some interior machinery including overshot waterwheel and an exterior undershot floodwheel. Footpath
goes close by.

3.35 Brightling Mill   TQ 686201
Sawmill which was driven by an iron overshot waterwheel by Neeves.
Now in poor condition. Footpath nearby.

3.36 Cobbs Mill, Sayers Common   TQ 274189
An interesting nineteenth century rebuild. Overshot waterwheel (penstock
dated 1868) worked four pairs of millstones by layshaft drive. Machinery
by W. Cooper of Henfield. A gas producer and a Tangye single cylinder,
open crank, horizontal, four stroke engine were installed in 1906 to provide power when water levels were low.

3.37 Cockhaise Mill   TQ 376258
Now a house. Retains waterwheel frame on north side.

3.32 Bishopstone Tidemill showing the three wheel culverts through which the tidal water passed

3.36 Cobbs Mill, Sayers Common

3.38 Deans Mill   TQ 354262
Rebuilt 1881. Last regularly used 1976 but still in working order. Iron
breastshot wheel driving four millstones. Can be seen from fisherman's
path on bank of river.

3.39 Duncton Mill   SU 964166
Stone and brick building with iron overshot waterwheel.

3.40 Wassell Mill, Ebernoe   SU 975277
Now a house. Retains overshot waterwheel but narrowed in width and
last used to generate electricity.

3.41 Fittleworth Mill   TQ 009184
An interesting building of local stone. Now gutted of most machinery.

3.42 Gibbons Mill near Bucks Green   TQ 072308
Old timber building on stone footings. All corn milling machinery
removed. Turbine installed c. 1900 to generate electricity.

3.43 Hurst Mill, West Harting   SU 765210
Interesting building with overshot waterwheel, now derelict. Corn milling
machinery gone. Last used for pumping.

3.44 Hellingly Mill   TQ 585125
Old timber framed building on brick walls. Three pairs of millstones on
T-shaped hurst. Remains of waterwheel 3 m wide, 2 m diameter.

3.45 Horsebridge Mill   TQ 582113
Old mill site, much rebuilt. Gutted but retains 5.2 m undershot waterwheel by Upfield of Catsfield.

3.46 Horsted Keynes Mill   TQ 381287
Timber framed building. A 5.5 m diameter wooden overshot waterwheel drove two pairs of millstones. Currently being restored to working
order.

3.47 Isfield Mill   TQ 448182
Nineteenth century building. Retains water turbine but machinery now
operated by electricity.

3.48 Moat Mill, Mayfield   TQ 591249
Now a house. Retains overshot waterwheel by Neeves of Heathfield.

3.49 Newbridge Mill   TQ 456328
Picturesque setting. Now a house.

3.50 Rackham Mill   TQ 046143
Interesting mill with remains of overshot waterwheel

3.51 Robertsbridge Mill   TQ 737241
Old mill site. Rebuilt in the nineteenth century. Retains remains of overshot waterwheel and turbine under present buildings. Now part of huge
animal feed complex.

3.52 Ruckford Mill   TQ 274190
Now a house. Retains two overshot waterwheels and milling machinery
by Cooper of Henfield. Upstream an interesting circular weir, visible from
the public footpath.

3.53 Sheffield Mill   TQ 416257
Long established mill on former iron working site. Old wooden lay-shaft
drive to two pairs of millstones but with more recent cast iron waterwheel
by Medhurst of Lewes.

3.45 Waterwheel, Horsebridge Mill

3.54 Steyning Court Mill   TQ 172115
Now a house. The oldest part at the west end retains an overshot water-wheel and basic gearing.

3.55 Trotton, Terwick Mill   SU 830222
Now a house. Retains two low breast waterwheels and most machinery.

3.56 Uckfield, Town Mill   TQ 475209
Interesting group of buildings showing the growth of business. Now gutted and used as a store.

3.57 Uckfield, Hempstead Mill   TQ 484217
Nineteenth century building with iron breastshot wheel, last used to drive generator.

3.58 Uckfield, Shortbridge Mill   TQ 451214
Nineteenth century building now gutted and being converted to a house. Retains cast iron backshot waterwheel.

3.59 West Ashling Mill   SU 807074
Interesting mill site. At one time a paper mill, then became a corn mill. Waterwheel replaced by Armfields turbine driving three pairs of millstones which together with auxiliary machinery survive complete. Formerly had a hollow post windmill above east end but of this only the back piers remain. Being converted into a house but machinery will remain.

3.60 Warnham Mill   TQ 168323
Fine building, stone lower walls then brick. Tile hung gable and a handsome Horsham stone roof. Large diameter iron and wood waterwheel. Basic machinery survives. At present being restored.

Mills on private land (appointment necessary)

3.61 Upper Mill, Plumpton   TQ 363147
Small watermill with iron overshot wheel which drove two pairs of stones. Being restored.

3.62 Plumpton Mill   TQ 363150
Mill with iron overshot wheel recently restored to working order. One pair of stones.

ANIMAL POWERED ENGINES

The use of animals to provide power goes back many centuries. Examples of the main types of animal powered machinery can be found in Sussex.

3.63 Brighton, Stanmer Park — horse gin   TQ 336095
Part of a small museum situated behind Stanmer Park House. It is sited in an open sided wooden building and was used for drawing water from a well. Two horses were used. Later converted to a gear driven pump. Dates from the sixteenth century. Can be seen when Stanmer Park is open.

3.64 Brighton, Stanmer Park — donkey wheel   TQ 336096
The wheel of 4 m diameter is housed in a small wooden building in the corner of Stanmer churchyard within the park. Used by the villagers to draw water from a well 76 m deep.

3.65 Brighton, Preston Park   TQ 305065

This horse engine is housed in a flint built, roofless building. Operated by a single arm (i.e. for one horse) is the two cylinder pump crank situated beneath the gearing frame and used for pumping water. Preserved by Brighton Corporation but not normally open to the public.

3.66 Saddlescombe near Brighton   TQ 273115

Donkey wheel 4.5 m diameter housed in slate roofed wooden building. For drawing water from a 23 m deep well. On private land in a small field next to a group of houses. Can be seen from the public footpath that passes nearby.

Singleton — Weald and Downland Open Air Museum (see 8.12) SU 874128

3.67 Donkey wheel from Catherington, Hampshire. Diameter 3.3 m and housed in a wooden building.

3.68 Horse gins:
    i. From Patching. Single shaft to drive gearing connected to a machine for grinding animal feedstuff.
    ii. Gin with single shaft to drive pugmill to mix clay for brick manufacture.

3.69 Lindfield, Old Place   TQ 349259

The iron frame of a horse gin is now all that can be seen. This is mounted above a well situated in a private garden. Old Place is in the lane that runs behind the parish church. The frame can be seen over the garden fence.

4. ROAD TRANSPORT

The earliest evidence of road communication in Sussex are the trackways across the South Downs, especially that which follows the ridge from east to west. The clay valleys north of the Downs were not easily traversed especially in winter. The Romans however drove Stane Street (the A 285, then A 29) from Chichester to London and developed a network of local roads sometimes serving iron working localities.

4.01 Holtye Roman Road
A 30 m length of road uncovered in 1939 and maintained by the Sussex Archaeological Society. It dates from the end of the first century, and the surface is of slag from iron working. Note the wheel marks and camber.

Parish initiative in the centuries that followed produced a network of roads maintained for local traffic, but a constant problem remained for wheeled vehicles in winter or after heavy rainfall. Travellers were however assisted by the construction of bridges, some of medieval date surviving in the western division of the county. On the line of the River Rother bridges of medieval date can be found at:

4.02	**Durford**	SU 783233
4.03	**Habin**	SU 808219
4.04	**Trotton**	SU 837223
4.05	**Iping**	SU 853228
4.06	**Woolbeding**	SU 873220

All are built of local sandstone and have been modified, repaired and strengthened during their working lives.

BRIDGES

The most important Sussex bridges are:

4.04 Trotton Bridge   SU 837223
Of early fifteenth century date. Carries the A 272 over the River Rother. It has five arches, is soffit ribbed, has bold cutwaters and was built by Lord Camoys.

4.07 Greatham Bridge   TQ 032163
Eight small arches and one larger. The latter was replaced by timber in 1839 and in turn by the present wrought iron girders in 1869. Following the 1912 Traction Engine Act a new centre pier was built to halve the girder span.

4.08 Stopham Bridge   TQ 029183
The finest medieval bridge in Sussex. It carries the A 283 road over the River Arun and was built in 1423 by the Barttelot family with the aid of a bequest from the Rev. Thomas Hayling, Rector of Pulborough. The centre arch was raised in 1822 to allow access for high loaded barges to the Wey and Arun Canal, and both ends of the bridge were extended in the 1860s.

4.09 Old Shoreham Bridge   TQ 207059

A fine trestle bridge of 26 piers and trestles built in 1781 over the River Adur. The causeway approaches are of stone. Built with the receipts of a tontine to replace a ferry and a toll was charged. Acquired by the Brighton & Chichester Railway under the terms of its 1844 Act. Carried the A27 traffic until the mid 1960s when the road was diverted and a new bridge built. At this point the tolls were discontinued and it became a foot-bridge only. It forms an attractive picture with the nearby Norman church.

4.10 Lewes Bridge   TQ 419102

An elegant brick and stone arch bridge carrying the road over the River Ouse and connecting the main settlement of Lewes with the Cliffe suburb. Designed by Nicholas Dubois, architect of Stanmer House in 1727. An overhanging footway was added to the north side in 1808 and another on the south side 1931–32 when the bridge was widened from the original ten foot carriageway. Best viewed from the Phoenix Causeway.

4.11 Exceat Bridge   TV 514993

This bridge of 1876 carries the A259 over the River Cuckmere. It has a span of 17 m and is constructed of wrought iron plate girders. The bridge was later strengthened internally, but its original appearance was pre-served apart from the addition of a footway on the upstream side.

4.12 Bodiam Bridge   TQ 783253

A fine brick bridge of three segmental arches spanning the River Rother at the south end of the village. Built in 1796 to replace an earlier structure.

4.13 Newenden Bridge   TQ 835270

Built in 1706 with three semi-circular arches. It carries the A28 road over the River Rother which at this point marks the boundary between Kent and East Sussex. The only stone bridge in the district.

Most of the objects of interest to the industrial archaeologist are those left by the turnpike trusts of which 52 were active in the county at their zenith in the early 1840s.

MILESTONES

The Acts of Parliament under which these trusts were established and maintained required them to set up distance markers every mile along the road. A number of these 'milestones' survive.

4.14 The 'Bow Bells' series extend along the A22 road from Lingfield (Surrey) TQ 364432 to Hailsham TQ 586084. They consist of iron plates attached mainly to wooden posts. An unusual feature of this road is the existence of two mile posts within a short distance of each other at Wych Cross both showing 35 miles to London. Improvements to the road were made in the early nineteenth century avoiding Tilburstow Hill, Godstone and extending its length slightly. The milestones on the northern part of the road (the City of London to East Grinstead Trust) were repositioned, but the Lewes to Wych Cross trustees declined to move theirs forcing the former trust to order a post indicating 35 miles from London which they positioned a few hundred yards from the original one (TQ 422316).

4.15 The 'Bow Bell' milestones from Uckfield (TQ 480198) to Hailsham display above the mileage figure a buckle, the badge of the Pelham family, important local landowners.

4.16 'Bow Bell' milestones (without the buckle) also cover the A26 road from Uckfield (TQ 475193) to Lewes (TQ 425116). Many of these, like those on the A22 date from the second half of the eighteenth century when the trusts were formed but others are more recent replacements.

4.17 The Union Point (Uckfield) to Langney Bridge Turnpike whose mile plates displayed the Pelham buckle extended from Hailsham along the B2104 road but used much smaller metal plates without the bells or buckles on this section. Only one early plate survives, No. 56 at TQ 586084. The others displaying distances 55 to 61 miles from London are recent reproductions.

4.18 A series of iron posts extend along the B2026 from Westerham (Kent) showing distances from London. The last four of these from Hartfield (TQ 477353) to Duddleswell (TQ 469310) are in Sussex. This turnpike was set up in 1767.

4.19 A series of iron plates attached to stone blocks extend along the A268 road from Flimwell to Rye indicating distances from London and Rye. Those in Sussex commence at Northiam (TQ 836270) and terminate at Rye (TQ 921214). This turnpike trust was set up in 1762.

4.20 At the entrance to the stable block of Petworth House (SU 976220) are two milestones from the Midhurst to Sheet Bridge Trust (established 1825). They were removed from their original locations soon after the commencement of World War II, in common with other direction signs. These two however found a new use protecting the masonry of the stone arch to the stable block which at that time was being used as a military supply depot.

4.21 The Petworth Turnpike Trust of 1757 placed its milestones in the front walls of cottages where possible and these survive at Northchapel (SU 953282), Petworth (SU 976213) and Duncton (SU 963181).

Isolated turnpike milestones exist elsewhere such as the sandstone blocks, in many cases sadly mutilated, at Wadhurst (TQ 608338 and 646309), Mark Cross (TQ 579296), Groombridge (TQ 530374), Broadbridge Heath (TQ 146317) and Southwater (TQ 160254).

Within the boundaries of corporate towns road maintenance was a local authority matter and corporations might also erect milestones.

4.42 An example exists in Lewes in the front wall of the Fifteenth Century Bookshop in the High Street (TQ 411100). The lettering on the rectangular stone plaque suggests an eighteenth century date.

A number of instances are known in Britain of country landowners erecting elaborate distance markers at the side of the public highway at the entrance to their country houses.

4.23 One Sussex example is to be found on the A275 road at the entrance to Sheffield Park (TQ 412247), where a tapering shaft with a fluted cap 2.8 m in height was erected c. 1780 on the instruction of John Baker Holroyd.

48

4.15 'Bow Bell' mile post at Framfield (TQ 489184) beside the A 22 road.

4.18 Mile post of the Westerham and Edenbridge Trust beside the B 2026 at Duddleswell (TQ 469310)

4.19 Mile post of the Flimwell Vent to Rye turnpike beside the A 268
at Peasmarsh (TQ 884230)

4.24 Milestones were sometimes incorporated in the walls of tollhouses. When Wych Cross tollhouse (TQ 419317) was demolished the sandstone panel giving the distance to Lewes was set in a brick frame on the site.

TOLLHOUSES

Tollhouses survive in a number of locations, in virtually all cases extended in size. Their original form was usually a two roomed cottage or bungalow. The best examples are:

4.25 **Midhurst** (Midhurst and Sheet Bridge Trust — 1825)   SU 874218
A brick bungalow with a tiled roof on the north side of the A272, originally of three rooms and with a centre projecting angled bay.

4.26 **Northchapel** (Petworth Trust — 1757)   SU 953296
A finely detailed brick bungalow of T-shaped plan, with tiled roof, on the east side of the A283. The toll board from this site is now in the Weald and Downland Open Air Museum, Singleton.

4.27 **Houghton** (Storrington and Balls Hut Trust — 1812)   TQ 023118
A flint bungalow with a slate roof, more recently extended and now used as a shop, on the north side of the B2139 at Houghton Bridge. A board attached to the wall gives the history of the tollhouse and turnpike trust.

4.28 **Storrington — Clay Lane Gate** (Storrington and Balls Hut Trust — 1812)   TQ 071134
A flint bungalow with brick banding and slate roof situated on the south side of the B2139.

4.29 **Long Furlong** (Worthing Branch Trust — 1802)   TQ 101075
This tollhouse, architecturally one of the finest in Sussex, is situated on the east side of the A280. It was built in the fashionable 'gothick' style, no doubt because of its proximity to Mitchelgrove House. Constructed of brick and flint with a castellated stuccoed front and slate roof. Originally one room downstairs and another above probably reached by a ladder in one of the turrets. A small office took up the front of the house with a centre window at which the tolls were taken. A 'gothick' stucco frame above the window originally contained the tollboard. Later extensions added at the rear.

4.30 **Blackstone** (Crouch Hill and Hurstpierpoint Trust — 1777) TQ 245173
A brick and weatherboarded bungalow with tiled roof, originally of three rooms. Very prominent plain chimney stacks. On the south side of the B2116.

4.31 **Hickstead** (Pyecombe and Hickstead Trust — 1808)   TQ 268203
A two storey cottage on the west side of the A23 just south of the minor road to Twineham. The cottage is of flint with brick quoins, the upper storey being weatherboarded. A side window to the north permitted approaching traffic to be observed. More recent additions at either end of the original cottage. The road has been re-aligned and the tollhouse now stands back from the road.

4.32 **Lindfield** (New Chapel and Brighthelmstone Trust — 1770)   TQ 347254
A rare example of an earlier cottage being bought by the trust. Two

A TABLE of the TOLLS payable at this TURNPIKE GATE.

[By the Local Act.]

	s	d
FOR every Horse, Mule, Ass, or other Beast (Except Dogs) drawing any Coach, Berlin, Landau, Barouche, Chariot, Chaise, Chair, Hearse, Gig, Curricle, Whiskey, Taxed Cart, Waggon, Wain, Timber-frame Cart, frame Dray or other Vehicle of whatsoever description when drawn by more than one Horse or other Beast, the Sum of Fourpence half-penny	"	4½
Such Waggon, Wain, Cart, or other such Carriage having Wheels of less breadth than four and a half Inches AND when drawn by one Horse or other Beast only the Sum of Sixpence (Waggons, Wains and other such Carriages having Wheels as aforesaid.)	"	6
FOR every Dog drawing any Truck, Barrow, or other Carriage for the space of One Hundred Yards or upwards upon any part of the said Roads the Sum of One Penny	"	1
FOR every Horse, Mule, Ass, or other Beast laden or unladen and not drawing, the Sum of Two pence	"	2
FOR every Carriage moved or propelled by Steam or Machinery or by any other power than Animal power the Sum of One Shilling for each Wheel thereof	1	0
FOR every Score of Oxen, Cows, or neat Cattle the Sum of Ten-pence and so in Proportion for any greater or less Number		10
FOR every Score of Calves, Sheep, Lambs or Swine the Sum of Five pence and so in proportion for any greater or less Number		5

[By 4, G.4, C.95.]

FOR every Horse, Mule, Ass, or other Beast drawing any Waggon, Wain, Cart, or other such Carriage having the Fellies of the Wheels of the breadth of Six Inches or upwards at the Bottom when drawn by more than one Horse, Mule, Ass or other Beast the Sum of Threepence		3
AND when drawn by one Horse, Mule, Ass or other Beast the Sum of Four Pence (Except Carts.)		4
FOR every Horse, Mule, Ass or other Beast drawing any Waggon, Wain, Cart or other such Carriage having the Fellies of the Wheels of the breadth of four Inches and a half and less than Six Inches when drawn by more than one Horse, Mule, Ass, or other Beast the Sum of Three pence three farthings		3¾
AND when drawn by one Horse, Mule, Ass or other Beast the Sum of Five pence (Except Carts)		5
FOR every Horse, Mule, Ass or other Beast drawing any Cart with Wheels of every Breadth when drawn by only one such Animal the Sum of Six Pence		6
Two Oxen or Neat Cattle drawing shall be considered as one Horse		

3 G.4, C.126

CARRIAGES with four Wheels affixed to any Waggon or Cart, pay toll as if drawn by two Horses, Carriages with two Wheels so ... pay tolls as if drawn by one Horse, but such Carriages are ... such Tolls if conveying any Goods or other than ... charge for Protection.

4.26 Tollboard from Northchapel toll now displayed at the Weald and Downland Open Air Museum at Singleton.

A 98 Lee Eaton's Silkhouse

storey timber framed building with brick infill of sixteenth or early seventeenth century date, now numbered 58, High Street and used as a shop. The gate was removed in 1884 and publicly burnt in the High Street.

4.33 Ashcombe (Lewes and Brighthelmstone Trust – 1770)   TQ 389093
A circular drum of coarse brown brick with a cement dome. Situated on the south side of the A27 near the turning to Kingston village. Probably erected *c.* 1810. An engraving of 1827 shows a similarly shaped building on the opposite side of the road with stuccoed walls, a classical porch and a brick extension to the rear. It is probable that the two buildings were originally *en suite*. The reason for this fashionable architectural display was the position of the tollhouse at the entrance to Ashcombe House. Lodges to fashionable country houses were often in this form, the living room being on one side of the drive and the bedroom on the other. Symmetry was considered of greater importance that the comfort of the inhabitants.

4.34 Malling (Malling and Witch Cross Trust – 1752)   TQ 426122
A brick bungalow with a centre projection and slated roof. On the west side of the A26.

4.35 Beddingham (Lewes to Eastbourne and Hailsham Trust
     – 1819)   TQ 463082
A small stuccoed bungalow with a slated roof used as a shop in connection with a petrol station. Built *c.* 1820 as a replacement for the tollhouse in Glynde village on the earlier Glyndebridge Trust, as the line of the new road by-passed this settlement. On the north side of the A27.

4.36 Laughton – Broyle Park Gate (Broyle Park to Battle Trust
     – 1766)   TQ 483128
On the south side of the A273 and originally a two storey brick cottage. It has subsequently been extended to the side and at the rear. A blocked lookout window can still be seen in the bedroom wall. The cottage was built some time after 1772, its construction being considered by a meeting of turnpike trustees in July of that year.

4.37 Amberstone (Broyle Park to Battle Trust 1766)   TQ 599113
A brick bungalow recently decorated with false timber framing on the south side of the A271. It displays two windows to the road flanking a now blocked central door. To the east is a lookout window and there is a modern extension to the rear. This gate was the scene of a fatal accident on 5 February 1805 when Lt. Thomas Donald Webb, riding a spirited horse given to him by his wife, lost control of the animal and collided with the toll gate. A memorial tablet to Lt. Webb is in Hailsham parish church.

4.38 Battle – North Trade (Broyle Park to Battle Trust
     – 1766)   TQ 738160
A brick bungalow with tiled roof. On the south side of the A269. It has been extended by a further bay to the west but otherwise is little altered externally. The observation window to the east is still *in situ*. In its original form it would have been very similar to Amberstone.

4.39 East Hoathly (Uckfield and Langney Bridge Trust
     – 1765)   TQ 523163
A stuccoed bungalow of T-plan with a slate roof. On the north side of

. . . . of the earlier part of the tollhouse

4.40 Horsebridge tollhouse

the A22 near the village centre. Little altered from its original form but now attached to a substantial Victorian house. This tollhouse also controlled a side bar across the road to Waldron.

4.40 Horsebridge (Uckfield and Langney Bridge Trust — 1754) TQ 577115
A small rectangular brick bungalow with a slate roof. On the north side of the A22 at the junction of the road to Hellingly. Two windows and a central door to the front (all replacements). Now used as a shop.

4.41 Swife (Ringmer and Hurst Green Trust — 1765)   TQ 616228
A bungalow of brick and stone construction facing the A265 road. It displays two windows to the road and is very similar to Amberstone which is contemporary in date.

4.42 Cade Street (Beech Down to Heathfield and Hood's Corner to Robertsbridge Trust — 1813)   TQ 606210
The Cade Street tollhouse is believed to be a two storey cottage which had subsequently been incorporated into a much larger house on the site. Its erection was authorised in June 1813 and all the houses for this trust were erected by James Lansdell of Battle.

4.43 Robertsbridge — Coldharbour (Beech Down to Heathfield and Hood's Corner to Robertsbridge Trust — 1813)   TQ 719235
A brick built two storey cottage with later additions at the back.

4.44 Wadhurst Lower Toll (Mayfield and Wadhurst Trust — 1767)   TQ 644313
A small brick bungalow with a tiled roof. On the south side of the A266. Two windows (one altered) to the road with a central doorway on the Amberstone pattern. A small, more recent, extension to the east. In 1978 it was derelict with no tiles on the roof.

4.45 Ticehurst — Burnt Lodge Gate (Mayfield and Wadhurst Trust — 1767)   TQ 685304
A weatherboard bungalow with a tiled roof. On the north side of the A266. Two windows with a central doorway to the front and a small extension, probably of later date, at the rear.

4.46 Ticehurst — Lower Gate (Mayfield and Wadhurst Trust — 1767)   TQ 695301
A substantial two storey cottage at the intersection of the A266 and A268. A late nineteenth century photograph shows that the toll board was originally displayed above the doorway, where a new window has been inserted. The tile hanging on the front and the extension to the north are also of a later date.

4.47 Compasses (St Leonards and Sedlescombe Trust — 1836) TQ 776204
A cottage partly brick and partly weatherboarded. On the west side of the A229.

4.48 Rye — Udimore Road (Brede Trust — 1771)   TQ 914204
A typical single storey two roomed tollhouse. On the north side of the B2089 adjacent to the bridge over the River Tillingham. Now used as a workshop.

TOLL BRIDGES

A number of bridges within the county were in the past subject to toll but in only one case does the tollhouse survive.

4.49 The Norfolk Bridge Tollhouse, Shoreham   TQ 213051

A fine suspension bridge spanning the River Adur was opened in May 1833. It was designed by W. Tierney Clarke who was also responsible for similar bridges at Marlow and Hammersmith. In 1922 this bridge was replaced by the present structure which carries traffic along the old line of the coast road between Brighton and Worthing. At the Shoreham end of the former bridge one stuccoed brick tollhouse survives with straight classical door and window pediments and a dentil moulding below the cornice. A pair of smaller collecting booths in the same style existed at the Lancing end of the bridge but were presumably demolished when the bridge was freed from toll in 1936.

FLYOVERS

Flyovers are not solely a feature of modern road engineering and two examples were produced early in the nineteenth century in the east of the county.

4.50 Cripp's Corner Flyover   TQ 776212

A sandstone arch erected *c.* 1841 to carry the line of the newly authorised Cripp's Corner, Ewhurst to Gills Green, Hawkhurst Trust (A 229) over the existing Brede Turnpike (B 2089). The original stone parapet has been replaced by iron railings. A similar flyover existed at The Harrow (TQ 798132) where the St Leonards and Sedlescombe Turnpike (A 28) burrowed beneath the earlier Flimwell and Hastings Turnpike. The banks of the cutting have in recent years been cut back to aid visibility and a new flyover erected which performs the same function as the demolished one.

COACHING INNS

The development of road passenger transport promoted by the new lines of turnpike encouraged the construction of inns capable of providing fresh horses and refreshment for travellers. A number of examples of very substantial inns built in the late Georgian period along turnpike roads exist. The best examples are:

4.51 The Shelley Arms, Nutley (A 22 road)   TQ 442281
4.52 The Sheffield Arms, Sheffield Green (A 275 road)   TQ 412249

In towns, too, inns and hotels developed in response to travelling. A good example of an urban coaching inn of this period is:

4.53 The Clarence Hotel, Brighton   TQ 311042

In North Street and now the headquarters of the Citizens Regency Building Society.

BUS AND TRAM SERVICES

The successful development of mechanical road transport from the late nineteenth century brought first the urban tram and then the motor omnibus. Examples of bus and tramway stations and depots exist in Sussex of which the most interesting are:

4.54 Tram depot, Bexhill Road, Hastings   TQ 778088

Now a centre for the sale of natural gas. This was the depot for that part of the Hastings Tramways which served West Marina through to Bexhill.

It is a typical red brick industrial building of *c*. 1905 without much later alteration.

4.55 Eastbourne Corporation Bus Depot, Churchdale Road   TV 622008

Dates from 1910 and is a good example of the industrial and commercial architecture of the day. Note the clever use of engineering bricks to give strength and decoration at strategic points. The adjoining small office building is quite out of character. Depot now disused.

4.56 Southdown Motor Services Booking Office, Cavendish Place, Eastbourne   TV 617991

An example of the 'express' and 'modern' image of coach travel in the late 1920s and early 1930s, this office is finished in green and cream glazed tiles.

4.57 Southdown Bus Station, Eastbourne   TV 615991

Situated in Pevensey Road and now used for shops and offices. The classically inspired art deco facade with circular first floor windows still survives. The original plan provided for two bus entrances/exits where the shop windows now are, with a first floor office and waiting room approached by a central flight of stairs.

4.58 Brighton Corporation Tram Depot, Lewes Road   TQ 325065

The original 1900 centre for the corporation tramways undertaking and still the bus depot for Brighton Corporation. The office building is little changed, even retaining the frosted glass windows inscribed with the tramway undertaking's name. The tram sheds have, however, been replaced by modern bus garages.

4.59 Southdown Bus Station, High Street, Bognor Regis   SZ 935990

An attractive art deco facade of the 1930s. Now converted into shops.

STREET FURNITURE

Street furniture of interest survives in a number of locations:

4.60 Ditchling Street Lighting   TQ 32/15

The Victorian cast iron lighting standards in the village streets have been augmented by a number formerly at Lewes station and dating from its construction in 1889. All have been converted from gas to electricity.

4.61 Petworth Lamp Standard   SU 977217

Situated at the junction of East and North Streets. Designed by Sir Charles Barry and erected in 1851. It is of wrought iron and mounted on a stone base and its style has been described as 'a cross between Gothic and sweet pea tendrils'.

4.62 Horsham Post Box   TQ 172304

Before the appearance of official pattern posting boxes in 1852 a number of postmasters provided privately commissioned boxes at their offices. One of these with a wooden hinged panel is to be found at the entrance to Pump Alley, Horsham. It bears the inscription 'Ye Olde Horsham Post Box' which is of course not contemporary with the period of its use.

Other Street Post Boxes

G.P.O. cast iron post boxes of early pattern are to be found in Brighton, Montpelier Road (First National Standard-Type 1859-66), St Leonards, Clyde Road (Hexagonal 'Penfolds' 1866--79). For the location of later Victorian and Edwardian boxes in Sussex, *see* Jean Young Farrugia, *The Letter Box* (1969).

5. CANALS AND NAVIGATIONS

5.01 WEY-ARUN
The River Arun was made navigable up to Pallingham (TQ 037214) by 1575, and the Arun Canal to Newbridge (TQ 068259) was opened in 1727. The Wey-Arun Junction Canal from Newbridge to the Wey was opened in 1816 and closed in 1868. The Canal was 23 miles long, 7.6 m wide and 1.2 m deep. Ten of the 26 locks survive. They are 3.7 m wide and 21.3 m long. The engineer was Josias Jessop, son of William Jessop. As most of the line of the Canal is intact a trust was set up in 1970 to restore it.

5.02 Hardham Tunnel   TQ 032175 to 033171
Built in 1790. The only canal tunnel in Sussex. Cuts across a three mile meander in the Arun. The north portal is best preserved, but access to the south portal is easier. Blocked in 1898 by the LBSCR because two of their lines ran over it (Pulborough to Arundel and Pulborough to Midhurst).

5.03 Pallingham Bridge   TQ 045221
Typical canal bridge, restored by the Trust. Carries a bridle way.

5.04 Orfold Aqueduct   TQ 058246
Has three brick arches. The west retaining wall is demolished. A copy of Josias Jessop's original drawing is on display in the Canal Room at the Chalk Pits Museum. The walls of Orfold Lock just south are almost intact. Best approached along the old towpath leaving the bridle way from Wisborough Green at TQ 051241.

5.05 Newbridge Warehouse and Wharf   TQ 068258
Dates from 1839. The brick warehouse is now a farm building.

5.06 Rowner Lock and Bridge   TQ 070271
Both restored by the Trust. Accessible by footpath from Paplands Farm or the A272 at Newbridge.

5.07 Loves Bridge   TQ 068276
Restored by the Trust. Accessible by towpath on the east side of the canal from Rowner Lock.

5.08 Malham Lock and Bridge   TQ 066288
The lock has been restored and a new bridge incorporated at the downstream end to replace a derelict bridge upstream.

5.09 MIDHURST NAVIGATION   TQ 033182 to SU 887213
Opened in 1794 to link Midhurst and Petworth with the sea. Abandoned in 1888. Two miles of cuts and eight locks. Locks were sited at Stopham, Fittleworth, Shopham, Coultershaw, Ladymead, Lodsbridge, Moorland and Todham. The engineer was William Jessop.

5.10 Entrance to the Canal   TQ 033182
The point at which the canal leaves the River Arun is accessible by towpath and the canal is still visible.

5.11 Coultershaw Lock   SU 972195
The only easily accessible lock. Adjacent to the A285. The line of the canal is crossed by a brick arch bridge and the lock abuts the north parapet of the bridge.

...starting work at Brewer Lock (Wey & Arun Canal Trust)

5.12 Midhurst Wharf   SU 887213

The old wharf has a number of modern buildings on it and the basin is filled in. Just before the canal joins the basin there is an attractive brick arch bridge. The date 1794 is inscribed in the parapet.

5.13 THE PORTSMOUTH ARUNDEL CANAL   SU 826012 to
                                                    TQ 004038

The Sussex section runs from Birdham to Ford. There were two locks at each end. From Hunston to Ford little remains except an occasional depression in the ground. This section was 5.8 m wide at the bottom and 1.4 m deep. Opened 1823. A spur went north from Hunston to a basin just south of Chichester and this section and the Birdham--Hunston section were 9.1 m wide at the bottom and 2.4 m deep to allow sea-going vessels to reach Chichester. It was opened in 1821 and is still full of water.

5.14 Salterns Lock, Birdham   SU 826012

The entrance lock from Chichester harbour, still in use. To accommodate part of the rise and fall of the tide, it is abnormally deep. There is a derelict lock used as a weir to impound water in the canal at SU 838011.

5.15 Poyntz Bridge   SU 865023

The only remaining cast iron swing bridge of the six supplied by Tickell of Southampton in 1820. Now being replaced by a high level bridge to permit boat access to the Chichester spur. It will be restored and mounted on the foundations of a similar bridge at SU 859029, in working order, but normally locked open.

5.16 Chichester Basin   SU 858042

Maintained in good condition and full of water as an amenity.

5.17 ROYAL MILITARY CANAL   TQ 880130 to 900180 and
                                        TQ 930240 to TR 170350

Built in 1806 as a coastal defence during the Napoleonic Wars in two sections — Winchelsea to Cliff End and Iden Lock to Hythe. Hythe Museum have a set of Rennie's original drawings.

5.18 Brede Lock   TQ 919199

At the junction of the Rivers Brede and Tillingham. Designed to work both ways depending on whether tidal level was above or below upstream river level. Now derelict.

5.19 Iden Lock   TQ 936244

Gives access to the eastern section of the canal from the River Rother.

5.20 Playden Lock   TQ 933227

Constructed in 1844 to facilitate navigation on the River Rother. 3.8 m wide. Still in use.

5.21 THE ADUR NAVIGATION

(BAYBRIDGE CANAL)   TQ 189176 to 164207

In 1807 the navigation was improved to allow boats to reach Bines Bridge. The Baybridge Canal Act of 1825 authorised extension to Baybridge on the A 24 Horsham to Worthing Road. Two locks were constructed on the extension. Both still exist but are on private land and thus not available for public view. The following can however be seen:

5.21 Baybridge   TQ 164207

Remains of a wharf in the undergrowth alongside the A 24 road.

Plate 8 ... ... with quarries on west bank (2.40) and Cliffe road bridge (4.10)

5.22 **Bines Bridge** TQ 189176
The bridge and the wharf can clearly be seen beside the B 2135 road just below Partridge Green.

5.23 **THE UPPER OUSE NAVIGATION** TQ 419102 to 324280
The Lower Ouse below Lewes was used by vessels for many years before the Upper Ouse Navigation Act enabled boats to travel farther upstream. Following a survey by William Jessop in 1788 the navigation was opened to Sheffield Bridge in 1793 and after financial problems to Upper Rylands Bridge in 1812. It passes through some superb and remote countryside and provides fine walking by means of public footpaths. There are physical remains of all but two of the 18 locks as well as several wharfs and numerous cuts. The best preserved and most easily viewable are the following:

5.24 **Chalk Pit Cut, Offham** TQ 405116
Straight 400 m cut from the navigation to the foot of the scarp. The Offham chalk pit (see 2.34) was connected to the cut by an inclined railway.

5.25 **Hamsey Cut** TQ 407119
A straight cut of 800 m avoiding a long loop of the river. Crossed by a bridge to Hamsey Place Farm. Remains of the lock are evident just before the junction with the river.

5.27 Bacon Wish Lock (David Gibbs)

5.26 **Barcombe Mills**   TQ 433148
Two well preserved lock chambers 46 m apart and separated by Pike's
Bridge. The locks are now used as weirs and the navigation as a fish ladder.
5.27 **Bacon Wish Lock**   TQ 399241
Well preserved walls and an accommodation bridge where a cut rejoins
the river. It can be found by following the navigation from Freshfield
Bridge to Sheffield Bridge.
5.28 **Freshfield Lock**   TQ 385245
The lock chamber is clearly visible on the upstream side of the road
bridge opposite the *Sloop Inn*.
5.29 **Riverswood Lock**   TQ 337275
Also known as Ryelands Lock. The lock chamber of stone is overgrown
but is easily recognisable in the cut by the river as a latter passes under
the embankment of the railway.
5.30 **Upper Ryelands Bridge**   TQ 324280
The terminus of the navigation has long since been filled in but the
remains of the wharf are clearly visible. Two wharf cottages stand alongside the road near the foot of the railway viaduct.

6. RAILWAYS

The railway age came to Sussex with the opening in 1840 of the line between Brighton and Shoreham, and the main line from London to Brighton was opened throughout in the following year. The west coast line from Brighton was extended to Chichester in 1846 and an east coast line from Brighton to Bulverhithe (1846) and Newhaven (1847) was constructed. A spur was also built from Three Bridges to Horsham (1848). This was extended in 1859 to Petworth and four years later another line to Pulborough through Arundel was built to connect with the coast line. All the lines described were part of the London, Brighton & South Coast Railway which originated from an amalgamation scheme of 1846. The only other company to challenge the supremacy of the LB&SCR in the eastern part of Sussex was the South East Railway whose Hastings line from Tunbridge Wells had by 1852 linked with the east coast line of the Brighton company at Bulverhithe. The line from Hastings through Rye to Ashford opened in 1851. In the far west the London & South-Western Railway's Petersfield to Midhurst branch opened in 1864.

6.01 Brighton Station   TQ 310049
Built in 1840 on an artificial terrace created by the removal of thousands of tons of chalk from the hill. The terminus building was designed by the architect David Mocatta. Now without its fronting colonnade and hidden behind Victorian canopies. On entering the station the impressive curved train shed of 1883 can be seen, now painted in its original colours, a superb expression of Victorian art and engineering. Consists of two 34 m span bays and is 181 m long. Wrought iron lattice trusses supported on cast iron columns supplied by the Butterley Iron Works. Notice the hanging clock with the LBSCR monogram and the indicator board.

6.02 London Road Viaduct, Brighton   TQ 309056
Built in 1846 for the Brighton, Lewes and Hastings Railway. This curved brick viaduct has 26 semi-circular arches of 9.1 m span with a central elliptical arch of 15.2 m span over the London road. Total length is 357 m and it has a maximum height of 20 m. The viaduct took only 11 months to construct. It can be seen to advantage from any of the surrounding hills or from the main railway line. John Urpeth Rastrick, the Company's engineer, used vertical gaps in the piers to minimize weight.

6.03 New England Bridge, Brighton   TQ 309054
This bridge, which carries a two track goods spur, consists of four slender cast iron arch ribs cast at the Regent Foundry, Brighton. It was opened in 1852 and retains its original appearance despite internal strengthening with steel beams in 1892. One hundred metres west is a fine brick arch with side arches for pedestrians completed in 1841 for the main London to Brighton line.

6.04 Patcham Railway Cottages   TQ 297092
A typical pair of railway cottages built in the 1850s situated to the west of the main line as it emerges from Patcham tunnel. Features are the

porch and guttering extending across the dormer windows. This type of cottage is fast disappearing.

6.05 Clayton Tunnel   TQ 293126
Completed in 1841. Features an ornate brick north portal with castellated parapet, easily seen from the A273 road. There is an inhabited cottage immediately behind the parapet probably provided for the attendant who serviced the gas lamps with which the tunnel was originally lit. The tunnel runs straight for 2,072 m and has 11 brick ventilation shafts. The south portal is plain.

6.06 Ouse River Viaduct, Balcombe   TQ 323279
Completed in 1841. The most imposing structure on the Brighton line carrying the track 29 m above the river on 37 semi-circular arches. The total length is 434 m. The viaduct is of brick with stone facing and has two Italianate pavilions at each end. The engineer was J. U. Rastrick. Construction materials were brought up the Ouse Navigation (see 5.23 and 5.30). A walk beneath the viaduct will enable the tapering brick piers, pierced with vertical openings, which give the viaduct a slender appearance, to be viewed.

6.07 Three Bridges Station   TQ 288369
The buildings adjacent to platform 5 still reflect the appearance of the wayside stations built in 1840–41 for the Brighton Company. Of stuccoed brick, retaining the original classical door and window surrounds. Initially it was a single storey building without a platform and canopy. The canopy was constructed in 1860 and was one aisle of an overall roof between platforms 4 and 5.

6.08 Rowfant Station   TQ 324368
A charming building with a steeply pitched roof, ornamental plaster work on the chimneys and diamond glazed lattice windows. Built in 1855 as the only intermediate station on the Three Bridges to East Grinstead line. Note the porch which provided shelter for the waiting groom from the nearby Hall. The line was closed in 1967 and the station is now boarded up and overgrown.

6.09 Crossing-keeper's Cottage, Hamsey   TQ 407124
Built 1858 and typical of the period. Has a slate-hung wall facing the track, decorative barge boards and a porch. Stands on the original alignment of the Lewes to Uckfield line but has performed no railway function since 1868 when the route was altered to leave Lewes by a bridge over Cliffe High Street.

6.10 Buxted Station   TQ 497235
After the building of the main and east and west coast lines expansion continued but finances were restricted and a standard station design was used with variations, depending on the volume of traffic. Buxted was built in 1866 and is typical of this period. An unadorned two storey brick station house and single storey office under a slate roof. A small canopy on both platforms and entrance side gave limited protection to passengers. Note the contemporary railway houses alongside and the now increasingly rare Southern Railway concrete lamp standards on the platform. The footbridge dates from 1894.

6.05 Clayton Tunnel (John Blackwell)

6.11 Crowborough Station   TQ 535298

Rebuilt 1905–7 in the opulent style used from 1900 to the First World War, with extensive glazed canopies with characteristic looping valance (now cut square) and covered footbridge supplied by Young & Co. of Pimlico. Rolled steel joists rather than timber were used to carry the canopies and less decorative columns which were also used as rain water pipes. Note the station name in blue glass letters on the windows and the remains of a luggage weighing machine set in the platform to the left of the entrance door. The huge contemporary goods shed can be seen from the entrance.

6.12 Eridge Station   TQ 542345

A typical country junction, rebuilt 1881 with a bay to terminate 'Cuckoo line' trains from Hailsham which would connect with the trains to Tunbridge Wells West and London via Oxted. The station buildings were constructed on an overbridge. The two island platforms have substantial wooden buildings on each and a wooden canopy supported by decorative cast iron columns and brackets. Note the signal box and railway housing on the north side.

6.13 Imberhorne Viaduct   TQ 383378

On the East Grinstead to Lewes line which was opened in 1882. An impressive and solid nine arch structure in red brick which can be easily viewed from the road and path beneath it. The line was closed in 1958 but the Bluebell Railway have proposals for re-opening this section subject to planning consent.

6.14 The Bluebell Railway (Horsted Keynes TQ 371292 to Sheffield
Park TQ 403237)

A superb example of 'living industrial archaeology' with its stock of vintage steam locomotives and rolling stock. Well worth a visit on the annual Parade Day in May. Both stations dating from 1882 were designed by T. H. Myres in the Norman Shaw country house style, are tile hung and incorporate decorative plaster work. The junction station at Horsted Keynes had five platform faces with extensive glazed canopies supported on both iron and timber columns (those on platforms 1 and 2 were demolished many years ago). Note the platform buffet and the signal box with a small brick pump house which contained a pump to raise water from a stream to the water tank on top.

6.15 Battle Station   TQ 755155

Designed by William Tress for the SER Tunbridge Wells to Hastings line, opened in 1852. Built in the gothic style, reflecting the architecture of the Abbey. It has been sympathetically restored and apart from the chimneys is externally unaltered though marred by a later canopy. Note the attractive booking hall roof, baronial fireplace, gothic doors and sandstone arches to the platform.

6.16 Rye Station   TQ 918205

Designed for the SER by William Tress and opened in 1851. A splendid Italianate building with a recessed entrance under three arches. A large goods shed is situated to the west with the remains of a weighbridge. Note the typical South Eastern staggered platforms and signal box.

6.15 Battle Railway Station

6.17 Worthing Station   TQ 146034
To the east of the present station stands the original 1846 one of the Brighton & Chichester Railway. It is two storied, built of flint with brick quoins and door and window surrounds and has a slate roof. In 1869 a second station was built to the west and a section of the 'Midland Railway' style gabled canopy strangely survives outside the parcels office. The elaborate ironwork of the supporting columns should be noted. The present station dates from 1908.

6.18 Arun bridge near Rudgwick   TQ 094237
This bridge, which was built in 1865, is accessible along the trackbed of the former Horsham to Guildford railway closed in 1965. A single span cast iron girder bridge at embankment level is directly over the original brick arch which was never used as the embankment had to be raised to reduce the gradient before the Board of Trade inspector would pass the line as fit to operate.

6.19 Timberley Viaduct   TQ 032138
This viaduct of 1863 over the River Arun retains its original appearance although the cast iron approach spans have been strengthened internally. Total length is 161 m and it consists of 15 spans. The main span of 32.3 m is of wrought iron bowstring girders 4 m high and at 66 degrees to the river. On either side is a wrought iron plate girder span with unequal length girders to accommodate the skew. The top flanges are curved in cross section reminiscent of Brunel's practice. The remaining twelve 9.1 m spans are of cast iron on cast iron trestles. The viaduct presents a low profile.

6.20 Arundel goods shed   TQ 024064
Compared with the drab station buildings of the period from the 1860s to the 1880s, goods sheds were pleasingly proportioned with the distinctive semi-circular windows. The two storey design at Arundel was particularly fine, as are similar examples at Littlehampton and Seaford.

6.21 Woodgate – former station   SU 939043
A charming collection of buildings erected in 1846 of brick and flint in typical Brighton & Chichester Railway style. It consists of a crossing keeper's cottage with typical wooden porch but missing the lattice bay window that fronted the tracks. An example of this can be seen at Ferring (TQ 095032). The well preserved single storey station, with a two storey station house, served Bognor until the resort's branch was opened in 1864. The typical 1876 signal box completes the group, unique by still retaining the LB&SCR nameboard.

6.22 Petworth Station   SU 971191
The substantial weatherboard terminus station of the Horsham to Petworth line of 1859 still survives as a private house. In 1866 the line was extended to Midhurst.

6.23 Rogate Station   SU 805217
An intermediate station on the L&SWRs Petersfield to Midhurst branch of 1864. The simple Victorian station with its two storey house and single storey offices survives though the line was closed in 1955. It is now used as an engineering workshop.

6.27 East Hill Lift, Hastings

6.24 **Brighton – Volk's Electric Railway**   TQ 316038 to 332035
The first public electric railway in Britain and still operating today. It was
opened by Magnus Volk in 1883 and extended in 1894 and 1901 to Black
Rock on an 838 mm (2 ft. 9 in.) gauge. A third rail supply was introduced
c. 1893. The Paston Place and Black Rock stations with much of the per-
manent way date from 1947–48 but most of the cars, though successively
rebuilt, are of 1897 to 1901.

6.25 **Rottingdean Railway**   TQ 327034 to 369021
East of the Marina at low tide can be seen lines of concrete blocks cast
into the chalk which were the sleepers which carried two railway tracks
of 825 mm (2 ft. 8½ in.) gauge, 5.48 m apart, of the Seashore Electric
Tramway. This line was built by Magnus Volk in 1894–96 from the
Banjo Groyne to Rottingdean and operated between 1896 and 1901.
Traction current was drawn from an overhead cable and the cars were
raised on stilt like legs 7.3 m above rail level, running on four bogies,
hence the name 'Daddy Longlegs' which was popularly used.

6.26 **Hastings, West Hill Lift**   TQ 822095
A cliff railway of 1890 running through a tunnel partly formed by a
natural cave. The line is 152 m long and the gradient 1 in 3. Two cars
work simultaneously from opposite directions. Traction is now by electricity though formerly an oil engine was used. The lift is open in summer.

6.27 **Hastings, East Hill Lift**   TQ 828096
A cliff railway opened on 9 April 1903 and running through a cutting
81 m long with a gradient of 1 in 1.28. Before electrification in 1974 the
operation was by water balance, each of the two cars carrying a 600
gallon water tank which was filled at the upper station and emptied at
the lower, from whence it was pumped to the top again for re-use. The
gauge is 1,524 mm (5 ft.) and the line is operated during the summer.

7. PORTS AND COASTAL FEATURES
AIRPORTS

PORTS

All the Sussex ports that are active today are in river estuaries. Due to littoral drift the river mouths wandered slowly eastward until floods caused a breakthrough to the west and the process started again. In the eighteenth century harbour commissions were set up. Their most important task was to stabilise the entrances by training works but with the facilities and knowledge available at that time, this proved to be a long and costly process.

LITTLEHAMPTON

In 1735 a new cut was completed to the west of the old entrance and two river training piers were constructed. These structures finally stabilised the entrance, but appreciable further work has been done since. The LB&SCR built a 137 m wharf for a cross Channel service in 1863 but their operations ceased here in 1882.

7.01 Piers and jettywork   TQ 028012
The timber east pier is much the same length (67 m) and in the same position as that of 1735 though it has been rebuilt several times. What may be the remains of the original west pier can be seen at the foot of the fender piles at low tide.

7.02 The Oldest East Bank Wharves   TQ 026018
Most of the wharves have been reconstructed in steel sheet piling this century but there is a length of 1870 timber structure left. From the public yard at the south end of Surrey Street (in front of the *Britannia Inn*), the site of the oldest wharf is on the west. The wharf on the east side was built *c.* 1870. Both are now denuded of buildings and used as open storage for timber (Travis & Arnold). The flint and brick buildings on the other side of Pier Road were built as a steam sawmill by John Eede Butt & Sons (see panel on street frontage), in the later nineteenth century.

7.03 River Road   TQ 023021 to 023020
Between the 1981 footbridge (replacing the road swing bridge of 1908, which in turn had replaced the ferry of 1824) and McWester Marine are several small workshops. Only two of these are of interest and their riverside elevations may be viewed from the footbridge. The southern half of the large block is the earliest, with a stone 'T ISEMONGER/1830'. The northern half has large windows facing the river. The building is of two storeys and is of flint and brick with a slate roof. The cement rendered, single storey building incorporates a stone inscribed 'W OCKENDEN/ 1843'.

7.04 Old Railway Wharf (East Bank)   TQ 022023
This is situated north of the bridge. It was mostly built by the LB&SCR
in 1863. The only remaining building is the former Customs House of
1864-65 which was heightened and extended to the north in 1972.
Between 1863 and 1882 scheduled steamboat services ran to the Channel
Islands and France.

7.05 Climping Shipyard (West Bank)   TQ 022021 to 023020
The boat building yards of D. Hillyard and W. Osborne were initially laid
out in 1839 and were capable of building vessels up to 600 tons. Many of the
old sheds and an old wet dock remain but have been modified. There was
a rope walk along the landward boundary of the site, the building that
housed the machinery at the north-west corner still exists. Near this is a
two-storey building with a hipped roof that housed the steam sawmills.

7.06 48 Pier Road (East Bank)   TQ 028016
The town's first gas works were built here in 1847, strategically placed for
the receipt of sea-borne coal. Of this the flint and brick buildings remain
though no machinery. The works were subsequently moved to the site of
the modern gas holder when coal was delivered by rail.

   The maritime history of Littlehampton is displayed in pictures, maps
and ship models at the Museum, 12a, River Road. (Open May–September,
Tuesday to Saturday. October–April, Thursday to Saturday).

SHOREHAM

   The present opening through the shingle spit, with three piers, east and
west parallel to each other, and a triangular middle one, was made in
1817-21. However these piers have been entirely rebuilt in the present
century, and the east and west ones are considerably longer and on a
different orientation, while the middle one has been shortened.

7.07 Shoreham Lighthouse   TQ 235047
The simple stone lighthouse at the landward edge of the middle pier dates
from 1846. The lamp is in the Marlipins Museum in the High Street.

7.08 Customs House   TQ 243050
To the west of the lighthouse. Single storey building erected in 1886.

7.09 Locks   TQ 242049

7.10 Aldrington Basin   TQ 267047
In the period following the construction of the piers little attention was
paid to the eastern arm of the harbour which was allowed to silt up. In
1854 however a 915 m canal was constructed to allow ships to reach a
basin at Aldrington. An entrance lock of brick with a stone capping was
constructed in connection with this project but this was converted into a
dry dock in 1934 when a larger lock was built adjacent. A still larger lock
(The Prince of Wales) was added in 1956 to handle 4,000 ton colliers for
the Brighton B power station and the canal was widened and deepened.
At the same time two new curving breakwaters were built and the training
piers were reconstructed, moving the entrance 460 m seawards. The
western breakwater is 731 m long and the eastern breakwater 1,100 m
long.

7.09   Unloading cargo, Shoreham harbour

7.11 Kingston Railway Wharf　　　　　　　　　　　　　TQ 230050

This wharf was at several periods between 1822 and 1859 used as a berth for cross Channel steamers. From 1840 it was connected to the railway by means of an inclined plane but later the coast road was raised on a shallow arch to enable a spur line to be laid beneath. This arch was demolished in 1981. Two old warehouses at the east end of the wharf remain, possibly dating from the 1840s.

7.12 Southwick — Sussex Yacht Club　　　　　　　　　TQ 244050

Behind the former Southwick Town Hall is the oldest surviving riverfront building, erected as a malting in 1816, with the furnace at the west end, now the club's offices and the malting floor beneath a series of six hipped roofs. The walls of the building are of flint with brick quoins. It was probably converted to other uses in 1848 when Kingston malthouse (demolished 1971 TQ 232050) was opened. Adjacent, to the west, is Lady Bee Wharf with four brick, two-storey workshops or stores of *c.* 1860 of which there are similar ones to the north of the locks.

7.13 Fishergate Terrace　　　　　　　　　　　　　　　TQ 255051

A row of mid-nineteenth century cottages, flint and brick, at road level standing above other buildings which may have been for horses and carts of carriers. There is also a five storey granary or warehouse.

7.14 Aldrington Basin Warehouses　　　　　　　　　　TQ 243050

Immediately north of the basin are modern warehouses, but under the cliff remain four of what must have been a continuous row of 24 single storey flint and brick sheds or warehouses each under its own hipped roof and some 9.15 m by 3.66 m in size. They were probably built at the same date as the basin (1854).

For displays of pictures, maps and ship models illustrating the history of Shoreham harbour visit the Marlipins Museum, High Street, Shoreham which is open daily from May to September (TQ 215050).

NEWHAVEN

The mouth of the River Ouse was stabilised just to the east of Castle Hill in 1733 by training piers but in 1793 they were reorientated on the recommendation of John Smeaton. The cross Channel steamer services to Dieppe were transferred from Shoreham to Newhaven in 1849 to run in conjunction with the railway, and the LB&SCR and its successors have largely determined the evolution of the harbour since then. In 1855–66 a half-mile cut (TQ 444020 to 448012) was made to straighten the river and increase the tidal scour. The cast iron swing bridge at its southern end was demolished in 1976. The sea wall under Castle Hill with, at its west end, the breakwater (TV 447999 to 452993), curving out to sea for some 950 m were built in 1879–84 in concrete. At the same time the old east pier was replaced in timber and again rebuilt, this time in concrete, in 1927-29.

7.15 Railway Wharf　　　　　　　　　　　　TQ 448014 to 451005

During the past 20 years the car and lorry have supplanted the railway in carrying passengers and goods to and from the ships and most of the nineteenth century railway buildings have as a consequence been demolished.

7.15 Newhaven Harbour

The principal ones remaining are the marine workshops (TQ 448014) opened in 1878 on land recovered making the new cut, immediately south of the bridge, and the brick warehouse, with rounded roof, at TQ 451005 dating from 1890.

7.16 Newhaven Harbour Railway Station   TQ 446015
The present station was built in 1878 when the east quay was extended.

7.17 Bridge Hotel Warehouse   TQ 446015
Behind the *Bridge Hotel* is the bridge to Denton Island (created by the new cut of 1865–66). It is the successor to a drawbridge of 1783. Adjoining the hotel is the only surviving warehouse of the pre-railway waterfront. It is a two storey yellow brick building under a low hipped roof of slate. It probably dates from the 1820s and was formerly part of a brewery.

7.18 Lighthouse   TQ 440005
An hexagonal timber lighthouse some 3.68 m high and dating from the 1840s has been re-erected at Tideways School.

For material illustrating the history of the harbour visit the Newhaven Local and Maritime Museum at the West Foreshore, which is open on Saturday, Sunday and Bank Holiday afternoons between Easter and October.

RYE

An important member of the Cinque Ports in the Middle Ages but from the sixteenth century its trade began to decline because of the silting up of the River Rother. Attempts were made to establish a satisfactory harbour in the estuary of the river but with little success despite the efforts of Smeaton (1764) and Jessop (1779).

7.19 The Town Quay   TQ 918203
Lined with warehouses (see 2.41) of eighteenth and early nineteenth century date suggesting some trade up the river as far as Rye town this late.

7.20 Rye Harbour   TQ 949183
Attempts were made to develop a new harbour near the river mouth, 1¼ miles south-east of the town. An east pier was constructed at the mouth of the river in 1845. When the South-Eastern Railway reached Rye in 1851 they were compelled by Act of Parliament to contribute to harbour improvement works. They ran a branch to the harbour but little trade materialised. Since this period few attempts have been made to improve the harbour and the railway killed off most of the former coasting trade and diverted the former cross Channel traffic to the railway ports on the East Kent coast.

7.21 Beachy Head Lighthouse   TV 582951
The original lighthouse protecting this coast was the Bellé Tout erected in 1831 on the cliff top (TV 563955). It was however discovered that mist frequently obscured this light and in 1902 the present lighthouse was built at sea level. It is a circular tower of interlocking granite blocks curved in elevation and of 14.3 m diameter at the base and 7.1 m at the top. The lantern is 4.27 m high and the light has a range of 16 miles.

The dioptric revolves once per minute, it floats on mercury and is driven by a 215 kg falling weight.

7.22 Hastings, Fishermen's Hut   TQ 827094

A distinctive series of tall black clinker-built net houses, used for storing fishing gear. The traditional name for these huts is 'deezes'. They stand on the Stade or foreshore of the Old Town.

PLEASURE PIERS

The development of the screw pile by Alexander Mitchell made the construction of these piers practicable. It was first used in England by Eugenius Birch who was responsible for building 13 piers. A screw pile from his Bournemouth Pier of 1860 is on show at the Chalk Pits Museum at Amberley (8.01). Without these piers the shore lines and promenades of the Sussex resorts would be monotonous.

7.23 Bognor Regis   SZ 934987

Built 1865 and 305 m in length. Now derelict apart from the buildings at the shore end.

7.24 Worthing   TQ 149023

Built in 1862 and 293 m in length, the buildings are of the present century.

7.25 Brighton — West Pier   TQ 303041

Built 1866 and 340 m in length. The head was extended in 1893 and a concert hall built in 1916. The new entrance is of 1932. The pier is at present in a poor condition and closed to the public, but a trust is attempting to raise finance to restore this listed building designed by Eugenius Birch. The cast iron work has attractive embellishments.

7.26 Brighton — Palace Pier   TQ 314037

Built in 1899 and 540 m in length. The theatre was added in 1901 and the end pavilions in 1911. The architectural style of the buildings was inspired by Brighton Pavilion. This pier is a listed building.

7.27 Eastbourne   TV 618988

Built in 1870 and 305 m in length. It is a grade II listed building. The shoreward end was destroyed by a storm in 1877 and rebuilt at a higher level. The theatre was added in 1888 and the landing stage in 1893. The designer was Eugenius Birch.

7.28 Hastings   TQ 812091

This pier of 1872 by Eugenius Birch is 276 m in length. It has two landing stages. Major reconstruction of the buildings took place in the 1930s.

AIRPORTS

7.29 Gatwick Airport   TQ 285401

Now London's No. 2 international airport with building advancing to create a second terminal building to ease pressure on the existing one which was built in the late 1950s but greatly extended in recent years. Of the pre-war, much smaller, airfield a few buildings survive. The old control tower of 1936 by Hoar, Marlow & Lovett, circular and in the modern International Style is to be found to the south of the present airport cut off from it by the A23 road, together with a contemporary hangar. Nearby are the platform faces of the original Gatwick Airport station opened on 30 September 1935 as Tinsley Green but renamed on 1 June 1936. This station was closed when the new airport developed farther north on the site of the Gatwick race course and the race course station was rebuilt to serve the new development.

7.30 Shoreham Airport   TQ 205052

The site was first used for flying in May 1910 when H. H. Piffard began testing a biplane. In 1911 the Avro flying school moved here from Brooklands. It was used by the Royal Flying Corps to train pilots in the First World War and by Miles Aircraft Ltd. between the Wars. In the early 1930s the municipal authorities of Brighton, Hove and Worthing set up a joint committee to establish an aerodrome. The Shoreham site was acquired in 1933 and work on the new terminal building commenced in 1934 though not officially opened until 1936. A number of RAF units used the field in the Second World War. It is now used for private flying in the main and a number of small factories connected with the aircraft industry exist. A concrete runway has recently been laid. Apart from the terminal buildings a number of temporary 1940s structures survive.

7.31 Ford Airfield   SU 989029

The hangars and buildings on the west side were constructed in 1916 (when the airfield was known as Yapton) and used by the Royal Flying Corps and US naval units. In 1928 the Ford Motor Co. took over the site with the intention of operating passenger air services to the Continent, and Henry Ford renamed the airfield after the local village of the same name. The hangars and accommodation on the east side were built during the pre-1939 expansion. Standard pattern hangars with wooden 'Belfast truss' roofs and a number of small buildings still survive.

7.32 Tangmere Airfield   SU 910050

The site was taken over by the government in 1917 for use as a flying training ground. It was intended ultimately for the US Air Force but the termination of the conflict made this use unnecessary and it was closed in 1919. Reopened in 1925 and had a continuous period of service with the RAF until its closure in 1970. It formed an integral part of the country's air defence system particularly during the Battle of Britain. A spread of buildings remain and an aviation museum has been established in one of the 1930s pattern hangars.

7.33 Westhampnett (Goodwood)   SU 875074
7.34 Merston   SU 885030

With the expansion of the United Kingdom air defences prior to the Second World War, two satellite airfields of Tangmere were formed. This increased the number of aircraft in a single geographical area and spread the risk of airfields being put out of action. The perimeter tracks remain and Westhampnett became Goodwood motor racing circuit. Various wartime buildings can be traced.

7.35 Southbourne Aerodrome   SU 768063

Built in 1918 for the US navy. Completed but never occupied. Some of its buildings are now part of a small industrial estate.

7.36 **Middleton-on-Sea**   SU 979000

An aircraft factory built *c*. 1914 for White & Thompson Ltd. (later
Norman Thompson Co. Ltd.) and closed *c*. 1919 after acquisition by
Handley Page Ltd. Now used as holiday camp.

7.37 **Rustington Airfield**   TQ 05/02

Built 1917–18 for the Americans but never fully operational. Now covered
by the Rustington Sea Estates. Two buildings remain, much altered and
turned into residences. The bungalow to the west of Sea Avenue entrance
was formerly the guardroom and the bungalow named 'Norton' at the
junction of Preston Avenue and Bramblings, the salvage shed. The hangars
were bought in 1922 by the Littlehampton boat builder Wm. Osborne, and
re-erected in River Road, Littlehampton where they still are. The water
tower is part of the later estate development.

7.38 **Friston**   TQ 535982

Fields were used in the 1920s as a landing ground, and in 1941 development as an airfield was authorised for Fighter Command. Some wartime
huts and storage buildings exist although there is no trace of the original
'Blister' hangars.

Advance Landing Grounds

To increase the number of military airfields in 1943–44, particularly to
provide air cover for the invasion of the Continent, a number of Advanced
Landing Grounds were constructed in the County. These consisted of a
natural earth surface reinforced with wire mesh with tented accommodation.
Some have reverted to farmland and their whereabouts only remembered
by local people. Others continue in use for private aircraft, gliding or sport-
ing flying. In Sussex they existed at Bognor Regis, Chailey (TQ 362192),
Coolham, Deanland (TQ 528120), Funtington and Selsey.

8. MUSEUMS

The Chalk Pits Museum and the Weald and Downland Open Air Museum in West Sussex and the Engineerium in East Sussex have a national reputation and have much to interest the industrial archaeologist. There are however many other general museums in the area that have relevant items and these are listed below.

8.01 Amberley — Chalk Pits Museum   TQ 028118
This is the Southern Industrial History Centre and its displays feature local crafts and industries including quarrying and lime burning and a working printer, potter and blacksmith. There are displays showing the history of rural water supply, concrete technology, wireless, roads, stationary engines, narrow gauge industrial railways and printing. An archive and reference library are being set up. Situated next to Amberley railway station with ample car parking space.
    Open 11 a.m. to 6 p.m. Wednesdays to Sundays, April to October, with many specialist events at weekends. (See also 2.37).

8.02 Arundel — Museum and Heritage Centre, 61, High Street. TQ 018072
A privately run museum with good displays concerned with local personalities. Crafts and implements displayed in realistic settings. Open Easter to October, Tuesday to Saturday 10.30–12.30 and 2 p.m.–5 p.m. Sunday 2 p.m.–5 p.m.

8.03 Battle and District Historical Society Museum, Langton House,
    opposite Abbey Green   TQ 747158
This museum of local history has exhibits concerned with iron making, leather working and gunpowder manufacture. Open Easter to October, Monday to Saturday 10 a.m.–1 p.m. and 2 p.m. to 5 p.m., Sundays 2.30 p.m. to 5.30 p.m.

8.04 Bexhill Museum, Egerton Park   TQ 737072
Contains local history exhibits including those relating to the iron industry. Open April to October, Monday to Thursday and Saturday 10 a.m. to 1 p.m. and 2.30 p.m. to 4.30 p.m.

8.05 Hastings — The Fishermen's Museum, Rock-a-Nore   TQ 827094
A museum in a disused church amongst the fishermen's net drying shops with displays concerning the local fishing industry. Open Easter to September, Saturday to Thursday 10 a.m. to 12 and 2 p.m. to 5 p.m. (See also 7.22).

8.06 Hastings Museum and Art Gallery, John's Place, Cambridge
    Road   TQ 810095
This museum has informative displays relating to local history and the Wealden iron industry and its products. Open Monday to Saturday 10 a.m. to 1 p.m. and 2 p.m. to 5 p.m. Sundays 3 p.m. to 5 p.m.

8.07 Herstmonceux — Royal Greenwich Observatory
    Exhibition   TQ 647103
The exhibition is housed in the Castle and covers the fields of astronomy

and the history of telescopes. Open Easter to September, Monday to Friday 2 to 5.30 p.m., Saturday, Sunday and Public Holidays 10.30 a.m. to 5.30 p.m.

8.08 Horsham Museum, The Causeway   TQ 172304
Includes many items of industrial history as well as wheelwright's, blacksmith's and saddler's shops. Open Tuesday to Friday 1 to 5 p.m., Saturday 10 a.m. to 5 p.m.

8.09 Hove, The British Engineerium, off Nevill Road   TQ 286066
Originally Goldstone pumping station, built by the Brighton, Hove & Preston Water Co. immediately following its establishment in 1864. Two engine halls are connected by a single storey structure which houses the boilers. Initially there was only one engine hall in which was installed in 1866 a beam engine of 130 nominal horse power operating at 12 strokes a minute and pumping 130,000 gallons of water an hour from a 49 m deep well. In 1871 the operation was taken over by the local authority and four years later the additional engine hall built for a Eastons & Anderson beam engine of 250 horse power. This engine is steamed most weekends. The original coalstore has been converted into an exhibition hall and houses a very fine collection of model steam engines, locomotives and mechanical devices. There is also a re-erected Corliss engine of 1889. Open every day 10 a.m. to 5 p.m.

8.10 Lewes Museum of Local History, Anne of Cleves House, Southover
            High Street   TQ 412097
An outstanding collection of ironwork is contained in this museum. It is housed in an attractive timber framed sixteenth century house. Open April to October, Monday to Saturday 10 a.m. to 5 p.m., Sunday 2 to 5 p.m.

8.11 Polegate, Eastbourne – Polegate Windmill and Milling
            Museum   TQ 582041
This museum has an interesting collection of items related to milling. Open Easter to October, Sunday 2.30 to 5.30 p.m. Wednesdays (August only) 2.30 to 5.30 p.m. (See also 3.08).

8.12 Singleton, Weald and Downland Open Air Museum   SU 874128
Although really devoted to vernacular regional architecture, this museum has plenty to interest the industrial archaeologist – a water mill, two horse gins, a donkey wheel, a tollhouse, an excellent history of plumbing and a wind pump. Open April to September and Bank Holidays 11 a.m. to 6 p.m., October, Wednesday, Saturday and Sunday 11 a.m. to 5 p.m., November to March, Sunday 11 a.m. to 4 p.m.

8.13 Brighton, Stanmer Village Rural Museum   TQ 336095
Depicts rural life. This museum has blacksmith's tools, a donkey wheel and a horse gin as well as agricultural implements. Open Easter to October, Thursday 2.30 to 5 p.m., Sunday 10 a.m. to 12.30 p.m. and 2 to 5 p.m. (See also 3.64).

8.14 Tangmere Military Museum   SU 905061
This museum on the edge of the former airfield and well known fighter station, traces its history and particularly highlights the wartime contribution. A recent addition to the accommodation has provided room for a collection of engines and 'bits and pieces' of crashed aircraft (largely from the Battle of Britain) recovered by enthusiast groups. (See also 7.32).

8.09 The British Engineerium — Engine Beam.

8.09 The British Engineerium — Governor of the Eastons & Anderson
beam pumping engine of 1875

8.09 The British Engineerium — A Victorian Workshop

Sussex; Eastern Section
*(Reproduced with the sanction of the Controller of H.M. Stationery Office
— Crown Copyright reserved)*

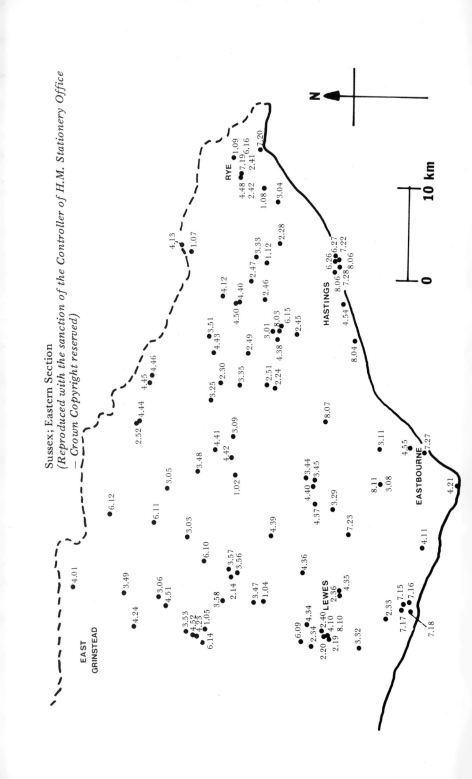

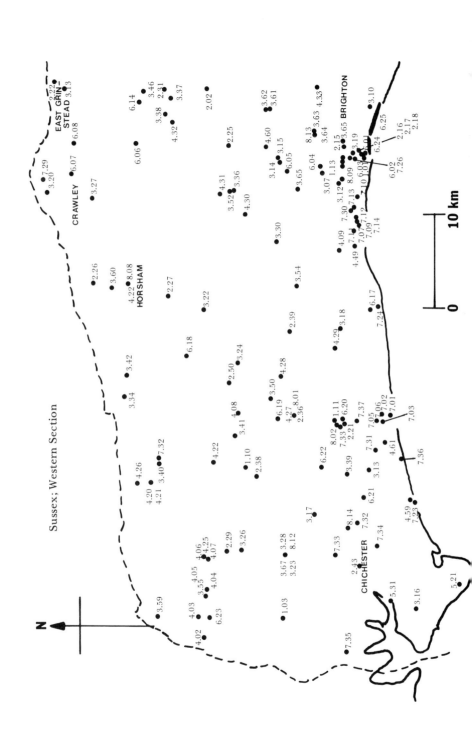

Sussex; Western Section

BIBLIOGRAPHY

The following books and pamphlets will provide a basis for the further study of the industrial archaeology of Sussex.

General

A. J. Haselfoot, *The Batsford Guide to the Industrial Archaeology of South-East England* (1978).
John Hoare & John Upton, *Sussex Industrial History: A Field Guide* (Chichester 1972).

Industries

Lyn Armstrong, *Woodcolliers and Charcoal Burning* (Horsham 1978).
G. H. Kenyon, *The Glass Industry of the Weald* (1967).
L. F. Salzman, 'Industries' in *Victoria County History of Sussex*, Vol. II (1907).
E. Straker, *Wealden Iron* (1933).
Henry W. Wolff, *Sussex Industries* (Brighton, n.d. 1883).

Roads

I. D. Margary, *Roman Ways in the Weald* (3rd edn., 1965).

Mills

Martin Brunnarius, *The Windmills of Sussex* (Chichester 1979).
G. M. Fowell, *Windmills in Sussex* (1930).
Peter Hemming, *Windmills in Sussex* (1936).
Richard & Richard McDermott, *The Standing Windmills of East Sussex* (1978).
— *The Standing Windmills of West Sussex* (1978).

Canals

Charles Hadfield, *The Canals of South & South Eastern England* (Newton Abbot 1969).
Ronald Russell, *Lost Canals & Waterways of Britain* (Newton Abbot 1982).
P. A. L. Vine, *London's Lost Route to the Sea* (Newton Abbot 2nd edn. 1966).
— *The Royal Military Canal* (Newton Abbot 1972).

Railways

Edwin Course, *The Railways of Southern England — The Main Lines* (1973).
— *The Railways of Southern England — Secondary and Branch Lines* (1974).
— *The Railways of Southern England — Independent and Light Railways* (1976).

Bibliography — *Railways* — *continued*

Adrian Gray, *The London to Brighton Line 1841-1977* (1977).

John Hoare, *Sussex Railway Architecture* (1979).

C. F. Dendy Marshall (revised R. W. Kinder), *History of the Southern Railway*, 2 vols. (Shepperton, 2nd edn. 1963).

J. J. Howard Turner, *The London Brighton & South Coast Railway*, 3 vols. (1977-79).

Conrad Volk, *Magnus Volk of Brighton* (Chichester 1971).

H. P. White, *A Regional History of the Railways of Great Britain* (Newton Abbot, 3rd edn. 1969).

Ports

John Farrant, *The Harbours of Sussex 1700-1914* (Brighton 1976).

For further information regarding industrial archaeology in Sussex readers should search national periodicals such as *The Journal of Industrial Archaeology, The Industrial Archaeology Review* and *Industrial Past* and for the history of transport in the county *Transport History, The Journal of Transport History* and the *Railway Magazine*. Publications concerning the history of Sussex, especially *Sussex Archaeological Collections* will be found useful, while the *Sussex County Magazine* and *Sussex Life* do from time to time contain relevant material. The only periodical exclusively concerned with industrial archaeology in Sussex is, however, *Sussex Industrial History* published by the Sussex Industrial Archaeological Society. Details of this and the *Newsletter* of the Society, which is also invaluable, can be obtained from the Hon. Secretary: R. G. Martin, 42, Falmer Avenue, Saltdean, Bright, BN2 8FG.

INDEX OF PLACES

page references in italics refer to illustrations

Clayton
  railway tunnel, 68, *69*
  windmills, 32
Coolham
  landing ground, 83
Coultershaw, *see* Petworth
Crawley
  Gatwick Airport, 81–2
  Gatwick Airport railway station, 82
  Ifield watermill, 35
  Lowfield Heath windmill, 34
  Three Bridges railway station, 68
Cripp's Corner
  Compasses tollhouse, 58
  flyover, 59
Cross-in-Hand
  windmill, 28
Crowborough
  railway station, 70
Crowhurst
  gunpowder works, 21, 25

Danehill
  Freshfield Lane brickworks, 9, *11, 12*
Ditchling
  street lighting, 60
Duddleswell
  milestone, 48, *50*
Duncton
  lime kilns, 17
  milestone, 48
  watermill, 42

Earnley
  windmill, 32
Eastbourne
  bus depot, 60
  bus station, 60
  coach office, 60
  lighthouses, 80
  pier, 81
East Grinstead
  malting, 7
  railway viaduct, 70
East Hoathley
  tollhouse, 55
East Marden
  village well, 1
Ebernoe, *see* Kirdford
Eridge
  railway station, 70
Exceat
  bridge, 47

Ferring
  railway cottage, 72

Fittleworth
  lock, 61
  watermill, 42
Flimwell
  milestone, 55
Ford
  airfield, 82
  canal, 63
Framfield
  milestone, *49*
Frant
  brewery, 6
Friston
  airfield, 83
Funtington
  landing ground, 83

Gatwick, *see* Crawley
Glynde
  lime works, 17, *19*
  tollhouse, 63
Greatham
  bridge, 46
Groombridge
  milestone, 48
Guestling
  brickworks, 9

Hailsham
  brewery, 6
  milestones, 48
  tollhouse, 55
Halnaker
  windmill, 34
Hamsay
  navigation cut, 65
  railway cottage, 68
Hardham
  canal tunnel, 61
Hartfield
  milestones, 48
  Newbridge watermill, 51
Hastings
  cliff railways, *73, 74*
  fishermen's huts, 81
  Harrow flyover, 59
  museums, 25, 84
  pier, 81
  tram depot, 59
Heathfield
  natural gas supply, 1
  Swife tollhouse, 58
Hellingly
  watermill, 42
Henfield
  Wood's watermill, 38

Herstmonceux
  observatory and museum, 84-5
Hickstead
  tollhouse, 52
High Salvington, *see* Worthing
Holtye
  section of Roman road, 46
Horsebridge
  tollhouse, *57, 58*
  watermill, 42, *43*
Horsham
  brewery, 6
  museum, 85
  post box, 60
Horsted Keynes
  railway station, 70
  watermill, 42
Houghton
  tollhouse, 52
Hove
  British Engineerium (Goldstone
  Pumping Station), 3, 85, *86–9. 95–7*
  West Blatchington windmill, 32, *33*
Hunston
  canal bridge, 63
Hurstpierpoint
  brewery, 6

Icklesham
  windmill, 28
Iden
  canal lock, 63
Ifield, *see* Crawley
Iping
  bridge, 46
Isfield
  watermill, 42

Keymer
  windmill, 34
Kirdford
  Ebernoe Common brickworks, 9, *13, 14*
  Wassell watermill, 42

Laughton
  steam engine from Glynde lime
  works, 17, *19*
  tollhouse, 55
Lewes
  Anne of Cleves House museum, 25, 85
  breweries, 4, *5,* 6,
  Cliffe bridge, 47, *64*
  granaries, 21, 22, *64*
  Malling tollhouse, 55
  maltings, 7

Lewes—*continued*
  milestones, 48
  station lighting standards, 60
Lindfield
  brewery, 6
  Cockhaise watermill, 38
  Dean's watermill, 42
  horse gin, 45
  tollhouse, 52
Littlehampton
  boatyards, 76, 83
  gas works, 76
  goods shed, 72
  harbour, 75–76
  museum, 76
Long Furlong, *see* Patching
Lowfield Heath, *see* Crawley
Loxwood
  Brewhurst watermill, 38

Malling, *see* Lewes
Mannings Heath
  hammer ponds, 25
Maresfield
  gunpowder works, 25
Mark Cross
  milestone, 48
Mayfield
  Argos Hill windmill, 28, *29*
  Moat watermill, 42
Maynards Green
  blast furnace site, *27*
Merston
  airfield, 82
Middleton-on-Sea
  aircraft factory, 83
Midhurst
  milestones, 48
  navigation, 61
  navigation wharf, 63
  Pitsham brickworks, 9, *10*
  tollhouse, 52
Mountfield
  gypsum mine and works, 25, *26*

Newenden
  bridge, 47
Newhaven
  harbour, 78, *79,* 80
  harbour railway station, 80
  lighthouse, 80
  museum, 80
  warehouse, 80
Newick
  brewery, 6
  village pump, 1